# GRAY HAIR AND BLACK IRON

⫴ ⫴ ⫴

## SECRETS OF SUCCESSFUL STRENGTH TRAINING FOR OLDER LIFTERS

*By*

BROOKS D. KUBIK

**Author of *Dinosaur Training:*
*Lost Secrets of Strength and Development***

The exercises, training routines and advice in this book are intended only for people of normal good health and physical condition. The exercises, training routines and advice in this book may not be for everyone. Always consult your personal physician before beginning this or any other exercise program, and always follow your physician's advice. In no way should this book be used to replace the advice from your personal physician. The author is not a physician, and this book is not and should not be construed as medical advice or as a substitute for medical advice.

As with any physical activity, there is always an element of risk for injury when one engages in this or any other exercise program. When practicing the exercises and in applying the routines or advice in this or any other publication, always practice safety, proper technique and common sense. Neither the author, publisher nor copyright holder will assume any responsibility for any accident, injury, illness, loss or damage that may result from following the exercises, routines or advice in this book.

The above comments apply to all persons. If you are over the age of 35, significantly overweight or have any medical condition or history of disease or illness, it is especially important for you to consult with your personal physician concerning this or any other exercise program.

Cover photo by Lily Faget.

# DEDICATION

To Trudi, with all my love.

To Mike Rinaldi (11/01/47—6/22/08).

To my father, Dick Kubik, who has been hitting the iron
for over half a century.

To all older lifters around the world—and to all the younger
lifters who will be there before they know it!

## TO ORDER ADDITIONAL COPIES

To order additional copies of this book, use the on-line order form at www.brookskubik.com or contact the author at:

Brooks Kubik Enterprises, Inc.
P.O. Box 4426
Louisville, Ky. 40204 USA

# CONTENTS

# FOREWORD

## By WILLIAM F. HINBERN

Take a good look at any mainstream "muscle magazine" that has ever been published and you will see that, for the most part, a certain group is rather conspicuous by its' absence.

And just what group is that?

Those over 40 years of age.

Once you hit 40, pal, you might just as well have fallen off the face of the earth as far as the mighty moguls of the muscle media are concerned.

Their target audience has always been, and still is to this day, the male in his teens and twenties.

Why? Because, generally speaking, this age group is still growing physically, lacking in self-confidence, impressionable, impatient, etc. They're desperate to get bigger and stronger—and that's something that's simple to teach—and they'll happily buy anything offered in the supplement ads (especially if there's a photo of a pretty girl in a bikini somewhere in the ad).

Now, there's nothing wrong with the muscle mags catering to the young guys. But there's something terribly wrong when the muscle mags virtually ignore the older lifter. After all, older lifters are people, too. And they have their own set of unique problems, issues, and questions.

Jack Palance put it best as the movie character, Curly, in *City Slickers*: "Growing old isn't for sissies." He was right.

If you're over the age of 40 and you're interested in hard, serious no-nonsense strength training workouts—then you know there's not very much reliable information for you out there.

But that's changed. This book has evened the score in a single volume. Because it's crammed with more training information specifically aimed at older lifters than any other book, course or manual ever written.

The book you are holding in your hands may very well be the answer to many of the problems that the aforementioned publishers have intentionally or unintentionally neglected and have failed to address from the fabled glory days of Louis Cyr and Eugene Sandow to the present.

This book is for those that have trained continuously for years but feel that what they have always done just doesn't cut it anymore.

It is for those that are seriously considering going back to the weights after a long layoff of many years.

Furthermore, it is for those that have never trained before at all, and would like to start, but have no idea how to go about it.

Sooner or later everyone, without exception, falls into one of these categories.

While middle age may introduce a whole new set of training problems, it doesn't have to be the end of your weight training career. You can still keep training and gaining. You just have to do it smarter and more efficiently than ever before.

If you want to add years to your weight training career then this book will truly be an eye opener.

The author has literally set an example with real life examples taken from his more than 40 years of weight training experience.

His training schedules and dietary recommendations may surprise you with their simplicity.

He dives head first into such controversial subjects as: machines vs. barbells; the best exercises for older lifters; training vs. straining; realistic goals; training smarter, not harder; avoiding injury; flexibility, stretching and athleticism; ground-based training; auxiliary exercises; quality vs quantity; "active rest"; cardio training with weights; focusing on what you can do, not what you can't do; and preserving and protecting your joints.

And he more than gives you your money's worth when it comes to information. In this one volume, you get more than 50 different training programs. There's literally "something for everyone" in this book.

He even serves up some practical advice on nutrition for the middle-aged lifter.

You may not be training anymore for the big game coming up this week-end, but you're training for a much more important game.

The game of life—and the only way to win it is to train sensibly and intelligently for life-long strength and health.

Finally—something that works for the mature lifter.

Finally—something for YOU!

*Bill Hinbern*
World Famous Weight Training Authority,
Author, collector and publisher of Strongman
memorabilia, books, courses, etc.
www.superstrengthtraining.com

# WHY I WROTE THIS BOOK

I wrote this book to provide concise, condensed and effective instruction on strength training and muscle building for men and women over the age of 40.

Peary Rader, the founder of *Iron Man* magazine, and the magazine's editor for 50 years, used to call the over-40 trainee "the forgotten man." He used the term because virtually all of the articles published over the past 100 years in the "muscle magazines" have been aimed at teenagers and young men.

If you think about it, Peary was right.

Consider the following. What are the two most popular topics for articles in the muscle magazines?

The first is how to gain massive amounts of muscular bodyweight as quickly as possible.

The second is the even more popular article about building big arms in record time.

Those are fine for the younger guys—the scrawny toothpicks who are desperate to pack on some serious muscle mass—but they don't speak to those of us who have labored long years in the Iron Mines and who are plenty big already.

Nor does it speak to those of us who work long hours at our job—who support our families and who struggle with issues like how to pay the bills or how to put the kids through college—who have limited time and energy for training—and who are more interested in how to train for lifelong strength and health than in how to gain 30 pounds of muscle in six weeks.

This book is an effort to even the score—to write something of value for older trainees—and to do it in a short, simple, easy to follow format.

This book is also an effort to speak to yet another group of forgotten lifters: the garage gorillas and cellar dwellers of the world, who toil in anonymity in home gyms featuring plenty of black iron and not much else. The modern muscle media doesn't have much to say to these men—and may not even know that they exist. But they're there—and they're the backbone of the Iron Game. Always have been, and always will be. They're my heroes. And I wrote this book for them.

That's why I wrote this book—and after you've read it, and applied its teachings, I hope you agree that it does the job.

# INTRODUCTION

It's an unusually cold winter evening in Louisville. A blast of frigid arctic air has roared out of the North, sweeping down and across the plains. A thick coating of ice covers the entire city. The streets are dark, slick and deserted.

I'm bundled in sweats in the middle of my garage gym. The house is built on a steep hill, and the garage is a separate building at the top of the hill. The wind hits it full force. Two small heaters do their best to fight the cold. They help, but only a little.

Not to worry. I'm playing the soundtrack to *Rocky Balboa*. Rocky's been a friend for a long time. I see him in my mind's eye, bundled in sweats just like I am, racing through a freak snowstorm with flakes the size of golf balls and bounding up the hard granite steps of the Philadelphia Museum of Art.

Those must be the most famous steps in Philadelphia.

Maybe in the entire world.

I was just 19 when the original *Rocky* movie came out. I was lifting weights in my parents' garage. Now I'm 52, and I'm still lifting weights in a garage. I guess some things never change. Of course, I do have a lot more gray in my hair than I had back then.

I've already finished a thorough 15-minute warm-up. Now it's time for my first set of power snatches.

I step onto the lifting platform and pick up my Eleiko barbell. The Swedish steel is cold to the touch. I wonder if it's as cold in Stockholm as it is tonight in Louisville.

I go through several sets of power snatches with the empty bar. It's all part of the warm-up. I want to be nice and loose when I begin hitting the heavier weights.

Then it's time for the first set with weight on the bar. I chalk my hands, step onto the platform—it's made of plywood sheets, topped with two thick rubber runners on each side, and measures 8′ × 8′—approach the bar, get set, and crank out five quick reps in the power snatch. They feel surprisingly good, and the bar doesn't feel quite as cold as it did a few short minutes ago.

The soundtrack is playing the world famous *Rocky* Theme. I know right then it's gonna be a good one.

For the next 60 minutes I hit it hard. Power snatches, snatch grip high pulls and front squats. The front squats put the fork into my already tired 52-year old body.

I finish my workout, turn off the heaters and the lights, and head back to the house. As I step out under the stars, I'm surprised to find that I'm covered in sweat.

The cold wind hits me and turns to steam. I breathe deeply, savoring the crisp tang of the night air. I exhale, and there's more steam. I can't believe how hot I am. What a great workout!

I know I'm not standing on the museum steps in Philadelphia. But it sure feels like it.

⽈ ⽈ ⽈

That was a great workout. And great workouts are the high points in the life of a serious lifter. They're part of what makes life worth living. Even if you're over the age of 40 and you've been hitting the iron for a very long time.

Since you're reading this book, I'm going to assume that you're a serious lifter. So you know what I'm talking about. There's your ordinary hum-drum, day-to-day existence where you get up in the morning, eat breakfast, shower and go to work—and there's work—and then it's the end of the work-day, and time to train. And that's the part of the day when you come alive. For a lifter, it's the best part of the day.

I was just a kid when the barbell bug snuck up and bit me in the butt. I've been training since I was 9 years old. I'm 52 now, and that means I've been hitting it for over 40 years of hard, heavy, result-producing workouts. Over the years, I've literally "tried it all." I've learned what works, and I've discarded the rest. I have plenty of valuable information for you.

In particular, I have information about serious training for older lifters. That's why you bought this book. You want to know how an older lifter should train. What exercises to use. What exercises to avoid. Whether to wear knee wraps and a lifting belt. How often to train. How heavy to train. Whether to use intensity cycling. How to warm-up properly. What sets and reps to use. How to train to avoid crippling soreness, chronic inflammation or over-use syndromes. How to avoid injuries—and what to do if you do get injured. What sort of diet to follow. How to keep your weight under control. How to stay motivated. How to combine cardio training and weight training. How to train in your 40's— how to train in your 50's—how to train in your 60's—and how to keep on going in your 70's and beyond. And that's exactly what I'm going to share with you in this book.

I'm not going to tell you that it's easy for an older lifter—and I'm not going to tell you I have a secret silver bullet that will make you feel like you were 17 all over again.

But here's something I'm going to promise you.

No matter how old you are, you can keep on training—and you can continue to get outstanding results from your training— and most importantly, you can continue to have FUN when you train.

So what are you waiting for?

Grab your sweats and your lifting shoes. Gear up and get ready for one great workout after another—and for many years of strength, health and happiness.

See you at the top of the museum steps.

# 1

---

# RECOVERY AND RECUPERATION
# FOR OLDER LIFTERS

The key to successful strength training for older lifters is recovery and recuperation. As we grow older, we need to change the way we exercise. What worked for us when we were younger doesn't work as well when we're in our 40's, 50's, 60's or beyond. However, if we train properly, follow a sensible diet and observe the other rules of good health, then we can train hard, heavy, seriously and with as much passion and enthusiasm as when we were beginners wrapping our hands around our very first barbell. This book summarizes the most important considerations for older lifters—and teaches you how to keep on training—and getting terrific results—at any age.

The training principles in this book apply to all older athletes, no matter what their particular training goals are or what type of training they prefer to follow. The principles in this book apply equally to Olympic weightlifters—to power lifters—to those who prefer strongman training—to athletes who are using weight training to improve their ability in their chosen sport—to bodybuilders—to those who just want to look better and feel better—to those who are simply interested in staying in good shape as they grow older—to men—to women—to cellar dwellers and garage gorillas—and to those who train at commercial gyms. If you're an older trainee, it doesn't really matter WHY you train. The same fundamentals apply no matter what your reason for training, your preferred equipment or the type of training you do.

⑊ ⑊ ⑊

Let's begin by discussing recovery ability and older lifters. And pay attention, because this is important. It may not be glamorous, but it's critical to your success as an older lifter.

You don't often hear the term "recovery ability"—and you rarely see the term in discussions about serious strength training for older lifters. But recovery ability is a critical concept. It's something you need to understand in order to get the most out of your training.

In simple terms, recovery ability is your body's ability to recover from the punishment you impose on it during a hard workout. If you train hard enough and heavy enough to stimulate strength gains and muscular growth, you actually cause damage to your body. You tear your muscle fibers apart, and you exhaust many of them. You place enormous stress on your body's connective tissue—on your tendons, ligaments and skeletal structure, and you work your heart, lungs and internal organs very heavily. As a result, your body needs to go into fast forward, overtime mode to repair the damage caused by your workout.

If you train within the limits of your recovery ability, your body is able to recover from a hard workout. And if your body has anything left over after the repair process has been completed, it will use the excess for muscular growth and for gains in muscular strength and power.

How long it takes to recover depends on a variety of factors—one of which is your age. Your recovery ability decreases as you grow older. That means that you may need extra time for the recovery process. It also means that even if you fully recover from a workout, you will have less recovery ability left over to support gains in strength, power and muscle.

Recovery ability varies from person to person, just as any other physical attribute varies. And you may be able to increase your recovery ability over time, as a training adaptation, and you may be able to increase it by improving your diet, taking fish oil capsules, taking whirlpool baths, icing your joints after heavy workouts, getting sports massage, going to an ART practitioner, getting other types of deep tissue massage, or similar methods. But all of us have limits, no matter who we are or what we do—and as we age, those limits drop lower and lower. As a result, a training program that worked great for you in your 20's may be a disaster in your 50's.

In addition—and this is critically important—your joints take longer to recover from hard training as you grow older. This means that even if your muscles have recovered from your training, your joints may still need additional time for full recovery. If you foolishly fail to give your joints the time it takes for them to recover, you are likely to trigger chronic inflammation that will make further progress impossible—and may very well lead to a serious injury.

In this regard, let me note an interesting point. Russian research on Olympic weightlifters states that "younger" lifters—in the 16–17 year old age range—can tolerate higher volume in their training than can "older" lifters in the 19–21 year old age range. If there's a significant difference in recovery ability between 16-year old lifters and 19 year-old lifters, then imagine the difference between a 16-year old and a 46-year old—or a 16-year old and

66-year old! I don't need Russian research to tell me that the older lifter is going to have enormously less ability to tolerate hard, heavy, high volume training than the younger lifter.

But that's where so many older lifters go wrong. They continue to train on programs designed for lifters in their teens or twenties. The result is always the same: the older lifter can't recover from the program, can't recuperate, and can't make any progress. He starts to get tired, irritable and nervous—and he develops nagging joint pain—and if he continues this insanity, he's almost certain to end up with a severe injury.

The bottom line is this: older lifters need to pay careful attention to recovery and recuperation. As you grow older, it takes longer and longer to recover from a heavy workout. If you train too hard, too heavy and too often, you won't allow for adequate recovery time in-between your workouts, and you'll quickly fall into a condition of chronic over-training. You won't gain very well, if at all, and you'll probably end up losing strength and muscle. You'll also end up with stiff, sore joints and constant aches and pains. And if the pattern continues, you'll set yourself up for an injury—possibly one that ends your lifting career. If, on the other hand, you take steps to maximize your recovery ability and to ensure that you recuperate fully from one workout to another, then you'll reap maximum benefits from your training at any age.

In later chapters, I'll discuss a variety of factors that affect recovery and recuperation for older lifters, including training programs, abbreviated and ultra-abbreviated workouts, training frequency, combining weight training with cardio training, exercise selection, sets and reps, diet and nutrition, fish oil supplements, rest and sleep, intensity cycling, how hard to train, psyching up, massage, ART and a variety of related topics. I'll also give you a series of detailed training programs designed to maximize recovery and recuperation for older lifters.

As you continue to read this book, keep the importance of recovery and recuperation firmly in mind. Everything that follows is intended to help you maximize recovery and recuperation.

# 2

## SHORTER IS BETTER: ABBREVIATED TRAINING FOR OLDER LIFTERS

As an older lifter, you can make the most of your recovery ability and maximize your recuperation by training with relatively short workouts. You don't need to spend long hours in the gym to get good results. In fact, as an older lifter, you'll do far better if you use shorter training sessions. Older lifters can get a terrific, result-producing workout in a very short period of time. My workouts typically last from 30 to 45 minutes. Some are as short as 15 or 20 minutes. A "long" workout is anything in the 45 to 60 minute range, and I almost never train longer than 60 minutes.

Let me repeat that. My workouts typically last 30 to 45 minutes. And I almost never train over an hour. That's not because I'm lazy, not because I don't like to train, and not because I have too many other things to do. It's because I've found that short workouts are a key to success for an older lifter.

Like most of you, I love to train. If longer workouts worked for me, I'd take longer workouts. But they don't work nearly as well as short sessions. There are several reasons for this. First, like many older lifters, I work long hours on a demanding job—or really, on two jobs, since I work a day job and also run a book publishing business. I simply don't have time or energy for longer workouts. Second, I find that I enjoy my workouts more if I go out to the garage, get warmed up and get it done. Third, I recover much better from shorter workouts. If I spend too much time in any one workout, I also end up paying for it the next day—or the next several days.

In this regard, it's worth mentioning that I keep detailed records of all of my workouts. As a result, I can easily tell what works—and what doesn't. When I train for an average of 30 or 40 minutes per session, I get stronger from workout to workout and continue making good progress for a long time. If I change my program and begin training for 45 to 60 minute sessions, I have a couple of good workouts and then begin to get stiff and sore and tired—and my form gets sloppy, especially on exercises like power cleans, power snatches and push presses—and then I begin to lose strength—and if I stubbornly keep at it, I always end up with some sort of nagging injury.

I'm not the only older lifter who's had good results from relatively brief, infrequent training programs and training schedules that allow plenty of time for recovery and recuperation. Clarence Bass is one of the best-developed Master's bodybuilders in history, and has written a series of books chronicling his diet and training from his late 30's into his 70's. Clarence has always subscribed to the HIT philosophy, and has followed programs consisting of short, hard, infrequent training sessions. But as he's grown older, Clarence has gradually reduced his training, and today, he's making terrific gains by following a divided workout program where he trains only two times every nine days. This allows him to maximize his recovery between workouts—and maximum recovery has played a key role in his success.

Another case in point is Fred Lowe, an outstanding Master's weightlifter who's won National and World Master's championships and set National and World Master's records in three different weight classes and multiple age divisions. In an interview with Roger LaPointe recorded shortly after Fred won his class at the 2001 National Masters, Fred noted that he had trained only twice a week for the contest. A two-hour session on Tuesday followed by a long soak in the hot tub, and a lighter, easier session on Friday that lasted 45 minutes to an hour. No, it wasn't much work—but that's the point. Fred focused on maximizing his recovery and recuperation, not on logging hours in the gym—and at contest time, the results showed.

## ABBREVIATED TRAINING FOR OLDER LIFTERS

Abbreviated training programs are programs consisting of five exercises or less. An example of an abbreviated program would be squats, power cleans and push presses—or squats, bench presses and barbell bent-over rowing—or squats, dips and pull-ups—or standing presses, squats, bench presses, barbell bent-over rowing and deadlifts. Abbreviated training programs have been around for a long time, and they've built tons of strength and muscle over the years.

Abbreviated training allows you to train hard and heavy, at high intensity, without exceeding your recovery ability. That makes it particularly beneficial for older lifters.

Abbreviated training lends itself to any type of training where you focus on hard work against heavy resistance. It works for Olympic weightlifters, for powerlifters, for strongman enthusiasts, for bodybuilders, for athletes and for everyone else. It works for those who prefer multiple sets of low to medium reps, such as the 5 × 5 system or the 5/4/3/2/1 system, it works for those who prefer heavy singles, and it works for those who train HIT style and take each set to the limit. It works for the guy who trains with an Eleiko barbell, the guy who trains with rocks, sandbags or barrels in his back yard, and the guy who prefers bodyweight training. But most of all, it works for older lifters— because it helps them maximize recovery and recuperation.

## ULTRA-ABBREVIATED TRAINING

I've used abbreviated training programs for much of my career, and I've gotten terrific results from them. As I've grown older, my workouts have become more and more abbreviated. My current workouts are what I call "ultra-abbreviated." In many of my workouts, I train only a single exercise. In other workouts, I train two exercises. Rarely do I do more than this in any one session. I enjoy ultra-abbreviated training because it allows me to get the most out of a particular exercise in a relatively short period of time. It also allows me to work hard and heavy without exceeding the limits of my recovery ability.

Another reason I enjoy ultra-abbreviated workouts is that they allow me to understand how my body is responding to the workout and to the exercise (or exercises) that I perform. If I perform a workout consisting of nothing but power snatches and the next day my shoulders or back are stiff, sore and aching, then I can safely assume that the power snatch caused the response—and I know I need to warm up better, drop the weight, work on my form, or perhaps switch to a different exercise. If I had performed a workout consisting of snatches, presses, power cleans, push presses or jerks, squats and bench presses, I probably wouldn't know what caused the problem.

And it doesn't have to be a problem that you're monitoring. For example, if I've been doing Trap Bar deadlifts for awhile and I switch to power snatches and power cleans, and my traps get sore, that tells me that the snatches and cleans are working my traps more than the deadlifts. Obviously, that's good information to know. Older lifters need to train as intelligently as possible, and the more data—and the more reliable data—you have at hand, the better.

I also like ultra-abbreviated workouts—usually consisting of hard work on a single exercise—because they allow me to start with extremely light weights and perform a series of progressively heavier warm-upsets until I reach my "working weight" for the day. I've found that I need more warm-up sets as I've grown older, especially on movements like power cleans, power snatches, and push presses, where timing, coordination and athleticism is so important, and on movements like deadlifts, Trap Bar deadlifts, and squats or front squats, where I work up to really heavy weights.

## DIVIDED WORKOUTS

For most of us, abbreviated training wouldn't work very well if we only performed a single exercise every time we trained. It might work for awhile, particularly if you were using a good all-around exercise such as the clean and press or clean and push press, but eventually it would begin to get boring—and boredom is one of the biggest enemies of training progress. In addition, you need a reasonable number of exercises to hit all of the major muscle groups in your body. So how do you train several different exercises and still follow an ultra-abbreviated program?

The answer is simple. Use a divided workout program.

In a divided workout program, you divide your exercises into several different workouts. The usual number is two or three different workouts, but you can use as many as six different workouts. Use a different workout every time you train.

For example, if you're a powerlifter, you might want to train squats, benches and deadlifts. If you prefer to train three times a week, you could do squats on Monday, benches on Wednesday and deadlifts on Friday. If you prefer to train twice a week, you could do squats and benches on Tuesday and deadlifts on Friday. If you want to add some auxiliary exercises, you might try squats and curls on Sunday, benches and barbell bent-over rowing or pull-downs on Tuesday, and standing presses (or push presses, dumbbell incline presses or close grip bench presses) and deadlifts or Trap Bar deadlifts on Friday.

# 3

## SETS AND REPS
## FOR OLDER LIFTERS

For the majority of older lifters, multiple sets of low reps are the most productive and least taxing way to train. Examples of multiple set, low rep training include the 5 × 5 system, the 5/4/3/2/1 system, and training programs based on triples, doubles and singles, such as 5–7 × 3, 5 × 3 followed by 1 × 2 and 1 × 1, 5–7 × 2, or 7–10 progressively heavier singles. Or you can train 4 × 5 or 5 × 5, followed by 3/2/1, 3/2, 3/1 or three or four progressively heavier singles. There are many variations of multiple set, low rep training, and the trick is to find the one that works best for you on any particular exercise. (And please note— what works best for you today will change over time—and what works best for you on any one particular exercise may not work best on other exercises.)

Multiple sets of low reps have several important benefits for older lifters. These include:

1. Better, more thorough and more efficient warm-ups.
2. More precise movement patterns.
3. Greater safety.
4. Reduced volume—which aids recovery and recuperation.
5. Easier on the joints.
6. Appropriate for athletic strength training, i.e., training programs that include power cleans, power snatches, push presses, jerks, and high pulls.
7. Increased bone density and tendon and ligament strength.

Let's briefly review each of these benefits of multiple set, low rep training for older lifters.

## BETTER WARM-UPS

Older lifters typically need to spend plenty of time warming up for their heavy sets. This includes both a general warm-up at the beginning of each workout and a specific warm-up for each exercise in the lifter's routine.

There's a famous story about the Russian weightlifting powerhouse, David Rigert. (Rigert was the Olympic champion in 1976, five-time World Champion, and set an amazing 68 World records over the course of his career.) Rigert was walking through the training hall the day after winning a major championship. He had been in the sauna, and was wearing swim trunks and sandals. He passed a barbell loaded to 275 pounds, flipped off his sandals, walked over to the bar, leaned over, grabbed it—and performed a perfect squat snatch with the bar. No warm-up—no light sets—no stretching—and no shoes! Just a perfect squat snatch with 275 pounds.

It's no reflection on Rigert's lifting ability to hazard a guess that he couldn't do that today, at age 62—and that he probably couldn't have done it at age 52—or age 42. Nor do I think he would even have attempted a barefoot squat snatch sans warm-ups with any appreciable weight on the bar at age 62, 52 or 42—because even champions grow older, and as they do, they grow tighter, stiffer and less flexible. (And if they have any past injuries or nagging dings and dents, then they need even more warm-up time.) That's why older lifters tend to spend plenty of time warming up before attempting anything close to a heavy weight in any exercise.

Most older lifters do best if they begin their workout with a ten to twenty minute general warm-up where they do plenty of stretching and mobility work for the areas they will be training in that particular workout. This can include performing their first exercise with a broomstick or an empty bar. For example, if I'm going to perform power snatches in a particular workout, I include plenty of power snatches with a broomstick, followed by power snatches with an empty bar, as part of my general warm-up.

After the general warm-up, the older lifter should perform a very light set of low reps in the first movement in his program, and work up in small jumps, doing a series of progressively heavier warm-up sets before he hits his first working weight of the day. Again, using the example of the power snatch, I might perform my first set with a pair of five kilo plates (66 pounds total, including the weight of the bar), and then work up in five kilo jumps. The progression from broomstick to my first working set might look like this:

| | | | |
|---|---|---|---|
| Broomstick | × | 3 × 5 | (part of my general warm-up) |
| Bar | × | 2 × 5 | (part of my general warm-up) |
| 66 pounds | × | 3–5 reps | (first warm-up set) |
| 88 pounds | × | 3–5 reps | (second warm-up set) |
| 110 pounds | × | 3–5 reps | (third warm-up set) |
| 132 pounds | × | 3–5 reps | (fourth warm-up set) |
| 142 pounds | × | 3–5 reps | (fifth warm-up set) |
| 154 | × | 3–5 reps | (first working set) |

Now, granted, that's a lot of warming up. On some exercises, you won't need to do as much. But remember, power snatches are an explosive, high-velocity, athletic movement, and I need to be as loose and flexible as possible when I do them—and I need to be well warmed-up for my working sets. That includes, by the way, a well-warmed up cardiovascular system—because performing a set of 3–5 reps with any sort of appreciable weight in the power snatch is a little like running a 50 or 100-yard sprint. Your heart and lungs will be working hard for the entire set. And you don't want to jump into a hard set of power snatches any more than you would want to jump into a series of hard sprints. Remember, you may think you're young at heart, but your heart is like everything else in your body—it's not as elastic as it once was. So give it some help, and if you do something that's going to impose a heavy load on your cardiovascular system, build a cardiovascular warm-up into your warm-up plan.

Now, as you can see, I've done a total of five light warm-up sets with broomstick and empty bar, followed by five progressively heavier warm-up sets. With that many sets, 3–5 reps per set is plenty. And doing a series of progressively heavier warm-up sets is way better for my body than would be a single set of ten or twenty reps with a light weight, followed by a big jump to my working weight. In fact, I'd probably cripple myself if I ever tried something that foolish—especially if I was doing a dynamic movement such as the power snatch or the power clean, or a heavy movement such as back squats, front squats, deadlifts or Trap Bar deadlifts. And so would almost any other older lifter out there.

## MORE PRECISE MOVEMENT PATTERNS

We've all heard the expression "Practice makes perfect" and we know from experience that it's true—in lifting, and in any other endeavor. But as Tommy Kono notes in his book, *Weightlifting, Olympic Style*, it's equally true that "Practice makes permanent." Meaning that if you perform a sloppy rep, you teach your body to perform sloppy reps—and if you do enough sloppy reps, you end up with a deeply ingrained sloppy movement pattern that will be difficult or impossible to correct.

This can be a huge problem for a lifter who performs high reps. A classic example is the lifter who insists on performing high rep squats or high rep deadlifts, and who finishes the set by "gutting up" the weight, with his back rounded and his knees moving out of position. That's a great way to teach your body improper lifting patterns—and a great way to hurt yourself.

If you want to lift weights in perfect form (as you should), then multiple sets of low reps are the way to go. When you perform multiple sets of low reps, working your way gradually and carefully up to your working weight, you are doing everything possible to re-enforce the proper movement pattern for whatever exercise you are performing. The light sets teach you the proper position for the heavy sets.

Multiple sets of low reps also allow the lifter to focus on perfect technique for his working sets PROVIDED the lifter uses a weight that allows a smooth movement on each and every rep. If you pile too much weight on the bar, you end up having to gut it up—and a slow, grinding, teeth-gritting lift is almost always going to be an ugly lift. (As we'll discuss later, there's a big difference between training heavy and training too heavy. Training too heavy is bad for everyone, but it's suicide for an older lifter.)

Multiple sets of low reps also help develop and maintain what I referred to in *Dinosaur Training* as "the success habit." Let's say you're doing back squats and you plan to perform five sets of five reps, starting light and working up to a heavy weight for your final set. (In this example, you'll perform four progressively heavier warm-up sets followed by one "working set" with your top weight.) In each set, you'll perform every rep in absolutely perfect form, with complete confidence and total control. This creates a sense of confidence that carries over to the heavy set. You're not just jumping into a heavy set that may or may not be possible for you. Instead, you're doing a series of progressively heavier sets where the final set isn't too much above your final warm-up set—and since you've nailed the warm-up sets and you're feeling strong and powerful, you just know you're going to be able to handle the final set the same way.

This is an important consideration for lifters of all ages, but it's particularly important for older lifters, who often have to fight those shadows of a doubt and other jokesters that like to come out and play on days when you're scheduled for a heavy squat workout but had trouble sleeping the night before, and when you did sleep, you tied yourself up in knots and woke up so sore and stiff you had trouble walking downstairs to get a cup of coffee.

## GREATER SAFETY

Most people think that medium and high reps are safer than low reps. I beg to differ. And I disagree most vehemently when we're talking about strength training for older lifters. For older lifters, low reps are the way to go. They're both more effective and much safer than medium or high reps.

Here's the reason. As discussed in the previous section, multiple sets of low reps help you train your body to move in a precise pattern on each and every rep that you perform. That has a double benefit. It makes each rep more productive, and it makes each rep safer.

The great lifting coach, Joe Mills, used to have a saying that summed it up pretty well. "The barbell doesn't jump up and hurt you!" Mills said. He meant that if you get hurt, you probably hurt yourself by performing exercises (or lifts) in poor form or by trying to handle weights that are simply too heavy for your current strength level.

Multiple sets of low reps help you to perform each rep in perfect form—and doing so is the best way possible to avoid an injury. It's also the best way to avoid unnecessary wear and tear on your body.

## REDUCED VOLUME

Multiple sets of low reps help to reduce your total training volume, which in turn helps your recovery and recuperation. Yeah, I KNOW that there is plenty of Olympic weightlifting material out there that teaches coaches to gradually increase an athlete's training volume as he progresses. But remember, this book is for older lifters, not for the young bucks. Older lifters need a reasonable amount of training volume (in part because they'll be doing plenty of progressively heavier warm-up sets on each exercise), but they must be very careful not to overdo it. After a point, training volume becomes too much of a good thing.

Training volume is measured by multiplying weight × reps and adding the total over the course of your workout. For example, a lifter's deadlift workout might involve the following weights, sets, reps and total tonnage:

$$135 \times 12 = 1{,}620 \text{ pounds}$$
$$185 \times 10 = 1850 \text{ pounds}$$
$$225 \times 8 = 1800 \text{ pounds}$$
$$275 \times 6 = 1650 \text{ pounds}$$
$$315 \times 4 = 1260 \text{ pounds}$$
$$350 \times 2 = 700 \text{ pounds}$$

Total Tonnage = 8880 pounds

Another lifter of about the same lifting ability might perform five sets of five reps per set, followed by one triple and one single. The weights, sets, reps and total tonnage for the second lifter's deadlift workout might look like this:

| | | | | |
|---|---|---|---|---|
| 135 | × | 5 | = | 675 pounds |
| 185 | × | 5 | = | 925 pounds |
| 225 | × | 5 | = | 1125 pounds |
| 275 | × | 5 | = | 1375 pounds |
| 315 | × | 5 | = | 1575 pounds |
| 340 | × | 3 | = | 1020 pounds |
| 360 | × | 1 | = | 360 pounds |

Total Tonnage = 7055 pounds

The first lifter performed six sets, 42 reps and lifted a total of 8880 pounds. Only six of those reps (a mere 14%) were over 300 pounds. (Based on the lifter's sets and reps, he's probably a 400-pound deadlifter, which means that 300 pounds is 75% of his one rep max.) If we measure his training intensity by calculating his average weight per set, it's 211 pounds. If we calculate his training intensity by using only the reps over 300 pounds, the intensity factor goes up to 326.6 pounds.

The second lifter performed seven sets, 29 reps, and lifted a total of 7055 pounds. Nine of his reps (31%) were over 300 pounds. On the basis of the entire workout, his training intensity is 243 pounds per set. If we do the calculation using only the reps with 300 pounds or more on the bar, it works out to be 328 pounds per set. And he finished the day with more weight on the bar than the first lifter. Put it all together, and the first lifter ends up doing 26% more work, while the second lifter is doing less work but training at a higher intensity. Both lifters have trained heavy enough to stimulate gains in strength and muscle, but the second lifter has done so with a much lower training volume, which means that he will use less of his recovery ability to recuperate from the workout—and that means that he has more "excess" recovery ability to support gains in strength, power and muscular size.

The difference between the two workouts was the lower reps performed by the second lifter. Rather than use the 12/10/8/6/4/2 pattern followed by the first lifter, the second lifter never exceeded five reps on any of his sets. The lower reps allowed him to train just as hard (or harder) as the first lifter, while significantly reducing his total workload.

## EASIER ON THE JOINTS

I think it was Tommy Kono, the legendary World and Olympic weightlifting champion, who first said, "You only have so many squats in you." Kono meant that your knees, hips and lower back can only stand a certain number of heavy squats over the course of your lifetime. Eventually, they wear out.

You don't have to be a lifter, or any other type of athlete, to see this phenomenon in action. It happens to plenty of people as a natural result of the aging process. That's why so many people are getting knee replacements, hip replacements, and shoulder replacements and having spinal fusion operations—at ever-increasingly younger ages. I can close my eyes and think about the people I know who've had a joint replacement operation (or several such operations), and create a pretty long list without even trying—and you probably can do the same thing. Heck, many readers of this book are probably walking around with more titanium rods than the Terminator.

There's a related phenomenon, which is this. I have no way of knowing if this is 100% scientifically or medically accurate—but I'll tell you the way it feels, and you can tell me if you agree. I believe that the reps you perform after a certain age count at least twice as much in the "wear and tear" column as the reps you performed at an earlier age. What's the line of demarcation? I'm not sure, but age 35 or 40 is close enough for most lifters (and in this regard, note that 35 is the year that Master's competition begins in Olympic weightlifting and 40 is the year it begins in most powerlifting organizations). Again, I have no research studies or medical journal articles to support this theory, but based on my own experience, I firmly believe it to be the case.

It all boils down to this. If you have a limited number of reps in you and a lifetime to use them, use them wisely and conservatively. It's like living off of an inheritance where there's a finite amount of money that has to last for your entire life. Don't squander it foolishly. Save it. Guard it. Protect it. Be conservative.

Don't do 10 reps when five will do the job. Don't do five reps where three will work. The joints you save will be your own.

## APPROPRIATE FOR ATHLETIC STRENGTH TRAINING

Later on, I'll discuss athletic strength training—workouts based on exercises such as the power snatch, power clean, high pull, push press and jerk. These exercises have enormous value for older lifters, and unless a prior injury, poor flexibility, balance or mobility challenges, or similar problems prevent you from doing them, you should include them as a regular part of your training—or even as the core of your training (which is how I use them). (If you can't perform athletic style movements, or if you prefer to use conventional strength training exercises, build your program around back squats, front squats, standing presses and deadlifts or Trap Bar deadlifts.)

Athletic strength training requires a very precise movement pattern for each lift. Instead of throwing the bar up and down for a set of non-stop reps, as many do with their weight training exercises, you perform a series of individual lifts. Each rep is a separate lift. A set is a series of reps (lifts) with a brief pause where you lower the bar to the floor (or drop it, if you are standing on a lifting platform and using rubber bumper plates), pause, get set, and then perform the next rep. There may be as much as ten to twenty seconds between each rep. You perform your reps in this fashion in order to begin each rep in exactly the right position. If you were to try to do a series of non-stop reps, you'd perform the first rep correctly and the ensuing reps incorrectly—which would reduce the effectiveness of the exercise, teach you improper lifting habits and expose you to injury.

For the same reason, you perform low reps when you use athletic strength training exercises. Very few lifters perform more than five reps when they are performing athletic strength training exercises, and many stick to triples, doubles and singles. If they try to do more reps, their form deteriorates, and they begin lifting the weight improperly—for example, beginning the initial (off the floor) pull with a rounded back, not starting the lift with their hips in the proper position, pulling the bar with their arms rather than driving it up with a combination of leg, hip and back power, jumping their feet too wide to catch the weight, and holding the hands too low in the receiving position of the lift.

In any event, multiple sets of low reps are really the only way to effectively train with athletic style exercises. Thus, if you use athletic style exercises, you need to use a program based on multiple sets of low reps.

## INCREASED BONE DENSITY

Multiple sets of low reps are a tried and true way to build bone density and tendon and ligament strength for lifters of all ages—and older lifters need to do everything possible to maintain strong bones, tendons and ligaments. In fact, that's one of the most important benefits of sensible strength training for an older lifter. We've all seen older folks (usually non-lifters) who spend their final years walking in bent, hunched-over fashion, using canes and walkers or wheelchairs, and falling and breaking a bone. You only have to see that sort of thing happen one time to one person to understand how important it is to keep your bones thick, hard and dense, and to strengthen your joints, tendons and ligaments as much as possible.

# 4

---

# MORE STRAIGHT TALK ON SETS AND REPS FOR OLDER LIFTERS

In the previous chapter, I talked about the various benefits of multiple sets of low reps for older lifters. In this chapter, I'm getting to get down to brass tacks and review some specific set/rep schemes and their appropriateness for older lifters. As discussed in the previous chapters, older trainees need to be very careful not to exceed their recovery ability. They also may have less energy than when they were younger. However, they usually need to perform more warm-up sets than a younger lifter. In addition, they may need to stimulate gains in strength and muscle by training with less than maximum weight (because using too much weight may cause extreme joint stiffness lasting for a week or more), which means they may need to do multiple "working" sets with weights in the 70% to 90% of maximum range rather than rely on one heavy set to do the job. Put it all together, and you see that an older lifter often needs to follow much different set/rep systems than when he was younger.

## WARMUP SETS

Take the question of warm-ups. When I was in my early 30's, I would take huge jumps on all of my warm-up sets in the squat, bench press and deadlift, moving from 135 pounds to 225 pounds to 315 pounds to 405 pounds in the bench press and up 495 or 585 pounds in the squat or deadlift. Often, I'd only do one rep per set, so I was hitting my top weights after only four or five warm-up reps. And I usually did very little in the way of a general warm-up. Looking back on it, I'm not sure how I lived through it—but somehow, I did.

It's twenty years later, and those days are gone for good. At age 52, I spend plenty of time on a general warm-up before I even touch the bar, and when I finally start lifting, I do MANY progressively heavier warm-up sets before reaching my working weight in any particular exercise.

In front squats, for example, I start with the empty bar and work up in 10 kilo (22 pound jumps) to my working weight. That ends up being a lot of sets, but I've found through trial and error that I need to do them. If I start higher—say at 132 pounds—or if I take bigger jumps and do fewer warm-up sets, I don't feel as ready for my working sets, I don't do as well on them and I end up with more dents, dings, aches and tweaks than if I take the 22 pound jumps and perform plenty of warm-up sets.

On the other hand, I don't need to perform very many reps on my warm-up sets. I sometimes do sets of five reps, but they're not necessary. Triples, doubles and singles work fine, and they reduce my over-all training time and total tonnage. So I often begin with one or two reps with an empty bar and work up in 22 pound jumps to my working weight—doing singles or doubles on each of my sets and working pretty quickly, with only short rest periods between my sets. I haven't seen that in any muscle magazines lately (or ever), but it seems to work pretty well. And it shows how things have changed, and how I've adjusted my training over the years.

## DOUBLES

When I get to my working weight, I have several options. One is to work up to my top weight for a double, and then call it a day. Another option is to work up to a weight that is close to my top weight for two reps, but not quite my maximum, and then stop. A third option is to perform five sets of two reps with a weight that is heavy but manageable for five doubles. On occasion, if I'm feeling really strong, I might do as many as six or seven doubles, but five seems to do the trick just as well. A fourth option is to work up to a heavy weight for two reps, then drop down by 20–40 pounds and work back up again in five or ten pound jumps. A fifth option is to perform two sets of two, add weight, do two more sets of two, add weight, and do one or two doubles to finish things off.

That's a huge change from my younger days when I would work up to one or two really heavy, gut-busting singles and then stop. When I was younger, I was able to do enormously heavy singles on a regular basis, and they provided plenty of growth stimulation. Today, I can't train that heavy on a regular basis without becoming ridiculously sore, stiff and over-trained.

I also can't get as over-the-top "psyched up" as I could when I was younger. Or at the least, I can't do it on a regular basis. And frankly, I don't want to. As an older lifter, I prefer to lift with muscle strength alone, than with muscle strength augmented by a strong "psych." It's always there if I need it, but I prefer to keep it in reserve. One of the keys to successful aging is to always leave some gas in your tank.

In addition, I've changed the exercises I do. I used to do more of a powerlifting program, and then I followed a program that combined powerlifting with heavy awkward objects and strongman training, as detailed in *Dinosaur Training*, which chronicles my training when I was in my thirties. Now I do power cleans, power snatches and similar movements taken from the arsenal of Olympic weightlifters. These movements require a very precise technique, and if I psych up too much before a set, I end up going out, yanking the bar off the platform and trying to heave it up in bad form.

For all these reasons, I've developed ways to stimulate gains in strength and power without using maximum or near maximum weights on a regular basis, as I used to do. I now prefer to stimulate strength and power gains by using weights that are challenging, but not impossible, and by performing more "working sets" than I performed when I was younger. That's the basis for the 5 × 2 system and similar approaches outlined above.

## TRIPLES

Of course, I don't always do five sets of two reps. Sometimes I do triples. In fact, I prefer to do triples on power snatches, power cleans, and high pulls, and sometimes on Trap Bar deadlifts. The first two reps tire me out and I have to concentrate extra hard on the final rep—and that one often becomes the very best rep of the entire set.

The protocol for triples is similar to the protocol for doubles. I can work up to a single triple with a heavy weight and then call it a day.

Alternatively, I can go almost as heavy—but not quite—and then perform multiple "working sets" with the same weight. Sometimes it's three working sets, and other times it's five working sets. Five triples with 80% of your one rep max is a very good workout.

## SINGLES

I often use singles, but I don't go as heavy (relative to my one rep max) as I did when I was younger. In the old days, I would almost always work up to my maximum weight or something very close to it. Now I rarely go over 90% of my one rep max. However, I usually do many more singles than I used to do. For example, on power cleans, power snatches, or power clean and press (or push press or jerk), I often do five singles with 80% of my one rep max, five singles with 85% of my one rep max, and five singles with 90% of my one rep max.

Other times, I'll work up to 90% and do five singles with that weight.

Another variation is to work up to my 90% weight, then drop down in weight and work back up again in five-pound jumps.

## FIVES

For an older lifter, sets of five reps are a big challenge when you're doing back squats, front squats, deadlifts, Trap Bar deadlifts and athletic style exercises. You may find that they're too demanding and you can't recover from them, especially on back squats and front squats. But they're definitely worth a try.

Fives give you a good balance between strength and power training and conditioning. If anyone claims you don't get any cardiovascular work by lifting weights, have the doubter try a few five-rep sets of power snatches. After he's gotten his breath back, ask him if he's changed his mind.

Five rep sets of the BIG exercises (back squats, front squats, deadlifts, Trap Bar deadlifts, power snatches, power cleans, etc.) are a lot like running a series of short sprints. That means your weight training workout has the same conditioning benefit as if you laced up a pair of running shoes and went out to the park or the high school track and knocked off some wind sprints.

Triples also have plenty of conditioning value, and so do doubles and singles, albeit to a lesser degree. But if you really want to strike a nice balance between your strength and power training and your conditioning, try some five-rep sets.

## 5/4/3/2/1 AND OTHER REP COMBINATIONS

Many lifters like to use set/rep schemes where they drop the reps as they add weight to the bar. Thus, you have the 5/4/3/2/1 system, the 5/3/1 system, and similar variations. Jim Schmitz is a big proponent of 5/4/3/2/1 for older lifters, and that alone ought to make you look into it.

Other systems combine fives, triples, doubles and singles. For example, you might do 5 × 5, starting light and adding weight on each set until you have to work pretty hard on the final set. You then add weight and do 1–3 triples. And if you're feeling extra strong, you might add more weight and do 1–3 singles.

Joe Mills used to have his lifters warm-up and then perform five reps on their first working set. They added weight and performed a second working set of five reps. Then they added more weight and did a final working set of five reps. If they felt strong, they added weight and did a series of progressively heavier singles, working up to their top weight for the day. That makes for a pretty rugged workout. In fact, many young and very well-conditioned Olympic lifters found that doing just two movements—the snatch and the clean and jerk—was all they wanted to do.

# 5

---

# TRAINING FREQUENCY
# FOR OLDER LIFTERS

We've touched on this topic already, but it's so important it requires a chapter of it's own. And if you've been paying attention, you probably have a good idea of what my suggestions are going to be—and why.

Let me begin by telling you about my own training. I usually lift three times a week, on Tuesday, Thursday and Sunday. Monday, Wednesday and Friday would work just as well, and so would Monday, Wednesday and Saturday or Tuesday, Thursday and Saturday. I prefer to train one day on the weekend because I don't work on weekends (other than writing books and articles about strength training), so I have more time and energy for training, and I usually hit it extra hard on my weekend training day. As far as training during the week goes, I prefer to lift on Tuesday and Thursday because that's what I've done pretty much my entire life. I grew up training in high school, college, and YMCA weight rooms, and at commercial gyms, and they all tend to be busiest on Monday and Wednesday (because our junior high and high school coaches always told us to train on Monday, Wednesday and Friday). When I trained in a weight room or commercial gym, I always tried to work out on days when there were fewer people and I could concentrate on my training and get a better workout. So Tuesday and Thursday became a habit back when I was in junior high school, and I've stayed with it ever since.

Like many other older lifters (Fred Lowe, Dr. Ken Leistner and Clarence Bass, to name just a few), I follow a divided workout schedule. I have three different workouts: Workout A, Workout B and Workout C. I perform Workout A on Tuesday, Workout B on Thursday and Workout C on Sunday. Each session is short and to the point.

On Tuesday, I focus on power snatches, followed by snatch grip high pulls. That's often all I do. I've tried following the power snatches with front or back squats, but quickly found that squatting three times a week makes my knees sore. Sometimes I follow the power snatches with military presses to help keep my shoulders strong and sturdy. Many older lifters neglect their shoulder training, especially overhead movements like military presses, and this can contribute to shoulder problems as you grow older.

On Thursday, I perform power cleans and jerks. I usually perform one jerk after each clean. Sometimes I perform my power cleans by themselves, followed by jerks from the rack. On occasion, I perform clean grip high pulls after the power cleans or the clean and jerks.

On Sunday, I perform front squats. Sometimes I just do front squats, and sometimes I perform military presses, push presses or jerks from the rack followed by front squats. I don't do back squats any more because (like many older lifters) my shoulders are pretty sore and beat up, and it's very difficult to hold the bar in the proper position. I suppose I could try using a Hatfield Bar or Dave Draper's Top Squat apparatus, but I enjoy doing the front squats and they give me a great workout, so for now, that's what I'll use for leg training.

I have another workout schedule that uses different exercises but follows the same pattern as my current program. In that schedule, I perform military presses, push presses or jerks from the rack on Tuesday, Trap Bar deadlifts on Thursday and front squats on Sunday. That's a terrific program, and if you don't do athletic strength training movements, this makes a very good program. It hits the main power zones (low back, thighs, hips and shoulder girdle) very hard.

Thus, I train three times per week, but only train each exercise one time or at most two times per week. If I performed more exercises in each workout, I might prefer training only twice a week. And as I grow older, I might find that I prefer twice a week training even if I stick to only one or two exercises in any given workout. (In fact, I've had a few weeks lately where I was only able to train twice a week due to work-related issues—and I actually felt really strong and extra-explosive on the twice a week schedule. So maybe it's time to give twice a week training a try.)

Hey, don't laugh. Twice a week training works really well for many older lifters. Have you ever heard of Fred Lowe? He's one of the top Master's weightlifters in the history of the sport—and he trained only two times a week to prepare for the 2001 National Championships.

Not every older lifter will do best on a program of two times per week training—but many will. There's a simple reason for that. Older lifters need to pay careful attention to recovery and recuperation. They must be very careful to train hard enough to stimulate growth without training so hard—either in volume, intensity or weight on the bar—that they find it impossible to recover from their workouts.

It's a fine line, and it gets more and more difficult to walk the line as you grow older. The ability to recover from heavy training varies from person to person, but one thing is true for everyone—it declines as you grow older. That's one reason why training programs that worked great when you were in your twenties or thirties don't work nearly as well when you're in your forties or fifties.

There are different ways to deal with the problem. One is to incorporate cycling or periodization principles into your training schedule. Another is to use a variation of the Light, Medium, Heavy system. Still another is to reduce your training to twice a week—or possibly even twice every eight or nine days. If you read Clarence Bass's books—which cover thirty years of his training career, and offer many interesting insights about how to adjust your training as you grow older—you'll see that Clarence eventually moved to two workouts every nine days—and found that he did far better on that program than on three workouts per week or even two workouts per week!

Here's a final thought. The great Olympic weightlifting coach, Joe Mills, used to say that doing three training sessions per week was ideal, and doing two workouts per week was better than doing four, five or six. And that was for coaching younger lifters. If he were dealing primarily with older lifters, Joe Mills might very well have suggested the twice a week approach.

# 6

---

# THE BEST EXERCISES
# FOR OLDER LIFTERS, PART ONE

Exercises are the tools of the trade for strongmen of any age—and that includes strongmen with gray hair—or those with snow white hair—or those who don't have any hair at all any more.

But like everything else in life, things change. The exercises you used when you were younger may not be the best exercises for you when you are older.

There are several reasons for that. First, an older lifter needs to scrap any exercises that cause joint pain, that irritate old injuries or that are likely to cause new problems. For many lifters, this means you need to drop many of the movements you loved to do when you were younger. (We'll talk more about specific problems that some lifters have with different exercises in another chapter—and we'll also discuss exercises you should avoid at any age.)

In my own case, I've dropped bench presses even though I was a five-time National Bench Press Champion and National and World age-group record holder in my early 30's (lifting in drug-tested competition, in the sub-master's division, 198 and 220 pound weight classes). I dropped the benches in my late 30's because they began to irritate my shoulders. Every time I performed a bench press with anything over 225 pounds it felt as if I had big, jagged shards of broken glass rubbing against the inside of my shoulder joint. So I realized I had two options. One was to keep doing bench presses and ruin my shoulders for life. The other was to drop benches and concentrate on overhead lifting and, hopefully, keep on training hard and heavy for the rest of my days. I decided to drop the benches. That's an example of what I'm talking about—and I wasn't even 40 when it happened. Lifters in their 40's, 50's and 60's will understand exactly what I'm talking about.

Second, an older lifter needs to concentrate on the exercises that have the most bang for the buck: compound, total body movements. Ground based exercises. To the extent possible, athletic style exercises (assuming you know how to perform them safely and correctly, and that you're not limited by any injuries).

## COMPOUND EXERCISES

Compound exercises are the best way for anyone to train—and that goes double for older lifters. The only exception is if you have an injury that keeps you from using a particular compound movement. (For example, if a shoulder injury makes it impossible to perform back squats, overhead presses, bench presses, power cleans or power snatches.)

Compound movements train your body as a whole. They teach your muscles to work together in an integrated, athletic fashion. That's why the late Patrick O'Shea described exercises like power cleans, power snatches, high pulls, deadlifts, push presses and squats as "athletic-type strength training" exercises. He believed that these movements were of tremendous value for older lifters—and that they were particularly valuable in combating the twin bugaboos of neuromuscular decline and power loss faced by aging athletes.

## PRESERVING NEUROLOGICAL FUNCTION

In *Quantum Strength Fitness II*, O'Shea observed (at page 261): "As each decade of life passes there occurs an erosion of neuromuscular function. This means we lose a little strength, speed and power leading to a gradual decline in peak athletic performance." O'Shea believed that athletes could fight this age-related decline by using athletic-type exercises in their training. He wrote: "Athletic-type lifts are mind/body exercises that significantly help maintain high level neuromuscular function over an extended life span. When power snatching or cleaning you are forced to think in terms of strength, speed and technique. This places the neuron/endocrine system into high gear, maximizing spatial summation, which is the primary means to increase strength. Neither bodybuilding nor machine training has the capacity to do this. *The bottom line is to train intelligently with athletic-type training.*"

Addressing the issue of declining power loss among older athletes, O'Shea noted (at pages 260–61): "The age-related loss of power (strength × speed = power) is not due so much to a loss in muscular strength as it is to a decline in movement speed. The primary reason for this decline is that the brain, specifically the cerebral cortex, is slower to process information necessary for executing explosive-reactive movements, such as the Olympic lifts,

43

or hammer throwing. . . . To slow down this loss of movement speed, one must continue to train with athletic-type lifts."

## CARDIO TRAINING WITH WEIGHTS

This topic is so important it deserves a chapter of its own—and it's going to get it later in this book. But right now, let me give you a brief glimpse of something that's extremely important for older lifters.

Athletic style strength training has a huge cardiovascular component—and you don't need to perform high reps to get there. Performing a set of five reps (or even a triple) in the power snatch, power clean or power clean and jerk is like running a series of short sprints. It's more than simply a way to build strength and power. It's a way to work your cardiovascular system. The same is true for deadlifts, Trap Bar deadlifts, back squats and front squats. For older lifters who need to focus on heart health and cardiovascular fitness, but who enjoy weight training and don't like "cardio," athletic strength training is the Holy Grail of strength and health.

## PRESERVING PERFECT POSTURE

One of the most important things to do as you grow older is to train the muscles that promote good posture. Exercises such as squats (performed with a flat back), front squats, overhead squats (for those who are flexible enough to perform them), deadlifts, Trap Bar deadlifts, standing presses (performed in military style), standing dumbbell presses, push presses, jerks, power snatches and power cleans help to promote and preserve perfect posture. For this reason alone, they're far more important for an older lifter than curls, chest exercises or triceps pumpers.

## PRESERVING ATHLETICISM AND MOBILITY

Many of us got started lifting weights in order to be better at football, baseball, wrestling, track and field, or whatever sport we played. That's how I got started. I wanted to get stronger for wrestling.

As we grew older and graduated from high school and college, most of us left our athletic careers behind us (unless we got involved in competitive weightlifting, powerlifting, bodybuilding or strong-man competition). We continued to train with weights because we enjoyed it, but we were no longer training to be better athletes. We trained because we enjoyed it, and because we wanted to be big and strong.

As an older lifter, it's time to return to the idea of training to improve our athleticism—not to improve our performance on the playing field, but to improve our performance in the game of life.

Being big and strong is great. There's nothing wrong with that. But as we grow older, we need to work hard on other equally important attributes. We need to maintain good balance. We need to preserve our flexibility. We need to train to be fast, powerful and explosive. We need to maintain our timing, coordination, dexterity and mobility. In short, we need to train like an athlete.

Too many older lifters fall into the habit of training on nothing but bench presses, incline presses, lat bar pull-downs, curls and triceps work. They choose these movements because they're easy, because they don't cause too much puffing and panting, because they don't stress the knees and lower back, and because they help the lifter build or maintain massive upper body development.

That's fine as far as it goes, but it neglects the entire concept of athletic training. It's an unbalanced type of training program that wouldn't work for an athlete, and it's a training program that doesn't do nearly enough for an older lifter. It's better than playing checkers, but it's far short of the best program for an older lifter. If you've been training that way, give yourself a pat on the back for hitting the iron on a regular basis—but do yourself a favor, and begin to train on a more balanced, all-around program that includes plenty of leg and back training—and plenty of athletic style exercises.

## MAXIMIZING HORMONAL ACTIVITY

Older lifters need to train in a way that maximizes the body's production of testosterone and growth hormone. Heavy compound movements are the tried and true way of promoting the body's hormonal activity. Movements like back squats, front squats, deadlifts, Trap Bar deadlifts and athletic style exercises (power cleans, power snatches, high pulls, push presses and jerks) trigger enormous increases in testosterone and human growth hormone. Isolation-style exercises have little or no effect on your hormonal system. So if you want to stay young and active, vigorous and powerful, aggressive and virile for your entire life, you know what exercises deserve the lion's share of your attention.

## GROUND-BASED TRAINING FOR OLDER LIFTERS

I'm a big fan of ground-based training for lifters of all ages—and it goes double for older lifters.

What do I mean by "ground-based training"?

It's simple. I'm talking about exercises that you perform while standing on your feet. The standing press is a ground-based exercise. So is the squat. In fact, all of the exercises that O'Shea described as athletic-type training are ground-based exercises—

which stands to reason, given the fact that you stand on your feet in virtually any sport.

Why is ground-based training important for older lifters?

It's important because it forces you to train in an athletic fashion—because it strengthens your bones—because it improves your posture—and because it helps you maintain your balance and coordination. Those things are important for anyone, but they're particularly important for older lifters. Remember, older lifters are fighting to maintain (or build) much more than strength, power and muscle mass—they're fighting to maintain neuromuscular control, the mind-muscle connection, and balance.

By the time they are in their 70's, many people can no longer walk. You see them shuffling along in walkers or hobbling along with canes—or scooting along in little mechanized chairs. In contrast, the famous turn-of-the-century strongman and wrestling champion, George Hackenschmidt, could jump over the back of a chair when he was in his 80's—and there are competitors in Master's weightlifting who demonstrate the same sort of athleticism on the lifting platform at age 60, 70, or beyond.

There's a remarkable video of a lifter named Arnold Khalfin on You-Tube. He's lifting at the American Master's Weightlifting Championship of 2007. It's amazing and inspiring. Khalfin is a former USSR National Champion and was the USSR team coach in Olympic weightlifting back in the early 60's—and he's still lifting today, in his 70's—and he lifts with tremendous speed, power and grace, using letter-perfect technique in the split style of snatching. He not only can walk, he can move like an athlete. And that's because he's been training like an athlete—using ground-based training—for his entire life.

As I write this, there's an article in a health and fitness column in the *New York Times* about the single most effective thing you can do to build strong, healthy ankles. What is it? It's simple. All you do is stand on one foot. Then stand on the other foot. Perform several "sets" with each foot. That's all it takes—and researchers say it's more effective than anything else you can do to strengthen your ankles—as well as keep your balance and coordination fine-tuned. If a simple ground-based movement performed without weights can be that effective, imagine what an entire program of ground-based movements with barbells and dumbbells can do for you!

## LEARNING HOW TO TRAIN LIKE AN ATHLETE

If you know how to perform power cleans, power snatches, high pulls, push presses and jerks, then do what I do: make them the core of your training program. If you don't know how to perform these movements, you have three options. One is to find a competent weight lifting coach who can teach you the fundamentals of Olympic weightlifting. *This is far and away your best option. Nothing beats one-on-one instruction with a competent coach when it comes to learning the Olympic lifts and related exercises.* You can find a coach by checking with your national Olympic weightlifting organization or with local weightlifting clubs. If you live in the USA, that means going to the USA Weightlifting website at <u>www.weightlifting.teamusa.org</u>, and checking the drop-down page that gives you local weightlifting clubs and local weightlifting committees. Use those as resources to find a coach in your area.

The second option is to try to learn the movements on your own, using books and DVD's to learn the proper method of performance. There are many excellent resources for those who are interested in athletic style strength training. One of the best is

Jim Schmitz' training manual, *Olympic Weight Lifting for Beginners and Intermediates*. It comes with an excellent companion DVD. You can order the manual and DVD from IronMind Enterprises at www.ironmind.com. Other excellent resources are Tommy Kono's book, *Weightlifting, Olympic Style* and Artie Dreschler's book, *The Weightlifting Encyclopedia*. Artie also has an outstanding companion DVD that goes with his book.

Note that squat cleans and squat snatches are extremely difficult to learn on your own—and often impossible to learn for older lifters who have less flexibility and mobility than when they were younger. Even experienced Olympic weightlifters often turn to power cleans and power snatches as they grow older. So if the squat style lifts seem daunting—or if you find that they're just impossible to learn—then feel free to stick to the power style movements. That's what I do, and it works fine.

Your third option if you have never done Olympic lifting and don't want to learn now—or if you suffer from old injuries that make the Olympic lifts potentially risky for you—or if you don't have the equipment or the space to train them—is to perform plenty of total body movements such as back squats, front squats, deadlifts, Trap Bar deadlifts, military presses and push presses. Combine these movements with bent-over rowing and your choice of bench presses or incline presses, and you'll have a very effective program. Some of the strongest older lifters I know train on schedules based on these exercises, and they get great results.

The key point is this: as you grow older, train like an athlete, not a bodybuilder. Don't drop your heavy, compound exercises and replace them with isolation movements simply because you're getting old. Of course, if an exercise hurts or if it irritates an old injury, don't do it. Replace it with something else. I've had shoulder problems since my high school wrestling days, and back squats are tough on my shoulders. So I do front squats instead. I used to do them weightlifter style, with the bar positioned on the front of the shoulders as if I was doing a squat clean, and that worked fine. But one day I simultaneously fractured and dislocated the middle finger of my left hand and severely sprained the other fingers and my wrist (in a non-lifting accident). While I was recovering, I couldn't hold the bar the conventional way, so I performed front squats with my hands crossed over the bar (bodybuilder style). It's just over a year since my injury, and my left hand and fingers are still too tight and stiff to hold the bar in the conventional style, so I continue to perform the movement with my hands crossed (although I'm gradually working back into the regular style used by weightlifters). That's a simple example of how to adapt and keep on training no matter what life throws at you.

## THOSE MARVELOUS MIRACLE MACHINES

You may have figured it out by now, but I'll come right out and say it. I'm not much of a machine guy. I went through a major Nautilus phase when I was a kid, and I slaved away dutifully on the Nautilus Pullover Torso machine, the Nautilus Double Shoulder machine, the Nautilus Biceps Curl and Triceps Extension unit, the Nautilus leg training machines and all the rest of them.

They claimed the machines were safer than barbells and dumbbells. They weren't.

They claimed the machines helped prevent injuries. They didn't.

They claimed the machines built strength and muscle many times faster than barbells and dumbbells. They didn't.

Let me give you a case history of what machine training can do for you. When I graduated from high school, my top weight was 155 pounds. At the time, I was training on Nautilus machines. My top bench press was all of 225 pounds.

During college, I continued to train on Nautilus equipment (and actually worked as an instructor at several different Nautilus clubs). I eventually dropped the Nautilus training and went back to barbells and dumbbells, training in a friend's home gym, then in a local YMCA weight room, and finally in my parents' garage. My weight went up to a high of 170 or 180 pounds, my bench press went up to 320 pounds, and I could clean and jerk 225 pounds.

For two summers in a row, following my junior and senior years of college, I worked an out-of-town summer job and had nowhere to train. I was trying to save as much money as possible for school, so I didn't eat very much, and my weight dropped to 160–165 pounds. So for me, in my late teens, 160–165 pounds was what I weighed when I was not training and was eating a very limited diet that left me hungry as the devil all the time.

After college, I went to law school, and was able to get back into serious training—as well as some serious eating in the university cafeteria. My weight quickly went from the post-summer low of 160 pounds to 180 pounds and my bench press climbed to 350 pounds.

During my second and third years of law school I lived in an apartment and was somewhere between dirt poor and flat broke most of the time. I didn't have much to eat, I was hungry most of the time, and I wasn't able to train very often. My weight gradually went back down to 163 pounds.

At age 25, I graduated from law school, and got a job with a law firm in Louisville, Kentucky. I rented a house that happened to be only a couple of blocks away from an old-school, heavy iron gym that featured something like a dozen York Olympic bars, tons of plates, and everything else you could want for a great powerlifting or bodybuilding workout. (No lifting platform, and no bumper plates, so Olympic lifting was out, and no strongman stuff because this was back in the days before people started

51

training with strongman implements. But the barbells, dumb-bells, flat benches and squat racks were all I wanted or needed at the time.) I trained three times a week, ate well, and shot back up to 180 pounds. My bench press went up to 360 or 365 pounds.

Then I moved, and the old black iron gym was a bit of a drive—and in a moment of temporary insanity I ended up joining a Nautilus facility located in a nearby tennis club.

I trained three times a week, pushing each set to the absolute limit, and finished each workout covered in sweat and rolled up into one little ball of throbbing pain. It was just the way the Nau-tilus gurus said to do it.

After almost a year of super-intense, balls to the wall Nautilus workouts, I stepped on the scales one morning and discovered that I weighed 163 pounds! The super-duper Nautilus program had caused me to lose 17 hard-earned pounds of muscle—and had taken my weight back down to what I weighed when I was working those summer jobs during college, not eating very much and hardly training at all.

Drive be damned! I went back to the old iron gym and started lifting barbells and dumbbells again—and my weight went right back up to 180 pounds. And from there, as I began to train harder and heavier—and to follow a divided workout schedule—and to use abbreviated training—my weight gradually went up to more than 200 pounds, and my bench press went up to a competition lift with 407 pounds and a bottom position bench press with 430 pounds (using a hard to manage 3″ diameter bar). (A lift I per-formed in a power rack, with bottom pins to catch the weight if anything went wrong—which is the only way to perform any kind of bench press, and in particular, the only safe way to perform a thick bar bench press.)

Today, at age 52, I weigh 225 pounds and I'm hard and mus-cular—and I'm strong—and I look at least ten years younger than my age. If I had stuck to the miracle machines, I'd probably weigh 150 pounds or less, and I'd look like a long-distance runner—and I'd be weak and scrawny, and I'd probably look like I was 60 or older. And that's the difference between training on miracle machines and training with barbells and dumbbells.

There are some other important differences, as well. Machines don't promote balance, coordination and athleticism. Barbells do. With very few exceptions, machines don't allow you to perform total body movements. Barbells do. Machines don't train the stabilizers. Barbells do. On most machines, you perform your exercises in a sitting or lying position. With barbells, you can perform an entire workout standing on your feet. Most machines don't do very much to build bone density. Barbells do. Machines lock you into a single range of motion, which either works for you or doesn't—and if it doesn't, you're going to hurt yourself. With barbells (and to an even greater degree, with dumbbells), you can use the best range of motion for your particular body structure.

Of course, if you're injured, you may have no alternative other than to perform machine training, at least for a while. And when you're very significantly up in years (as in, over 70), you may prefer machine training to no training at all—although that's not a given, and there are some outstanding Masters weightlifters and powerlifters out there who are still competing into their seventies, eighties and even nineties.

Finally, it would take a small fortune to equip a home gym with an array of exercise machines. In contrast, it's very inexpensive to set up a top-notch home gym for barbell and dumbbell training.

# 7

## THE BEST EXERCISES
## FOR OLDER LIFTERS, PART TWO

Put it all together, and the essential exercises for older lifters are the following movements, with everything else relegated to the status of auxiliary movements (which we'll discuss in the next chapter):

### BACK SQUATS

An old standby, and an exercise that most of you have been doing for a long time. Keep on doing it! Properly performed, the back squat builds strength, power and muscle—triggers hormonal activity—keeps your spine strong—keeps your knees, ankles and hips strong and supple—and helps you maintain balance, coordination, neurological efficiency and over-all athleticism. Plus, it's something that 90% of the young guys don't do in the gym (if they go to the gym), so it automatically puts you far ahead of them. Heck, it may even darken the gray in your hair!

You can perform your back squats powerlifting style—with the bar positioned low on your shoulders, and going down only until the tops of your thighs are parallel to the floor—or Olympic style, with the bar positioned high on your shoulders, and going down as far as possible. I prefer to do Olympic style squats. They promote greater flexibility in the hips and are a more direct leg and hip exercise than powerlifting style squats. However, if you have not been doing them, break in very slowly and gradually. You'll need to treat them as a new exercise if you've performed parallel squats in the past.

Always perform your squats with a flat back. Squatting with a rounded back puts enormous pressure on your spine and can lead to serious lower back problems. It also adversely affects your posture.

Whether you perform them powerlifting style or Olympic style, you can get tremendous benefit from back squats without putting an enormous amount of weight on the bar, and without performing slow, grinding, agonizing repetitions. Training the exercise regularly and consistently, in perfect form, with a reasonable weight, is much better and more productive than piling as much weight as possible onto the bar and then performing the exercise in poor form or "gutting it up." Older lifters need to learn to TRAIN, NOT STRAIN—on their squats, and on all other exercises.

By the way, older lifters should wear Olympic lifting shoes when they train. Your feet, arches and ankles need plenty of support, and these shoes are specially made to provide it. Lifting shoes have a high heel, and help you maintain an upright position when you perform Olympic style back squats. Don't leave home without them.

# FRONT SQUATS

Another excellent movement for lifters of all ages, and a particularly valuable movement for older lifters because it aids the development of balance, coordination and core strength. When performed without a belt, the front squat is a superb and very natural exercise for the abdominals and obliques.

For best results, learn to perform your front squats while holding the barbell in your hands, with the back of your hands resting on your shoulders (the way an Olympic weightlifter performs the exercise). This requires plenty of shoulder and wrist flexibility, and takes awhile to learn. Be patient, and work up gradually.

If this style of performance is too difficult due to flexibility issues, use the "arms crossed at the wrists" or "bodybuilder" style of performance.

Wear lifting shoes for your front squats. Unless you're super flexible, you won't be able to maintain the proper position without them.

# BENT-LEGGED DEADLIFTS

Another time-honored and time-tested strength builder. Many view the deadlift as second only to the back squat when it comes to building total body strength and triggering hormonal reactions from exercise. For older lifters, however, the deadlift is a two-edged sword. If the lifter trains too heavy and begins to round his back, then the benefits are largely mitigated and the deadlift quickly leads to lower back pain—and often to an injury.

To get the most from your deadlifts, perform them in perfect form, with your back flat throughout the entire movement, and always keep the bar close to your legs as you lift it.

As with the squat, you should use a weight that is challenging but nevertheless allows you to perform each rep smoothly and precisely, in perfect control. If you train too heavy, your form will break down—and then your lower back will break down—and that's not good! As an older lifter, you need to train for life-long strength and health, and that means you need to use your head when it comes to deciding how much weight to put on the bar.

Lifting shoes are a great addition to your deadlifting program. They help you maintain an upright, flat back position that gives maximum results with minimal stress on your low back and spine. And they help support your feet, arches and ankles in what will probably be the heaviest exercise in your training program.

## TRAP BAR DEADLIFTS

I cannot say enough good things about this piece of equipment. Invented by Al Gerard, a powerlifter and engineer, the Trap Bar is one of the most useful training tools for an older lifter. The unique geometry of the Trap Bar allows you to keep the weight lined up with your center of gravity for the entire lift. This allows you to train harder and heavier, with less stress on your spine, than if you were using a regular barbell—and for an older lifter, this alone can be the difference between productive training and throwing in the towel. There are lots of knock-offs and imitations out there, but you get what you pay for, and I like to go with the original. You can order the original Al Gerard Trap Bar from John Wood (who sells them under license from Al Gerard) at www. functionalhandstrength.com.

Older lifters will find the Trap Bar to be a hugely important exercise. This is because your center of gravity tends to shift forward as you grow older. If you train properly and keep your weight under control you can fight the aging process that causes the forward shift, but at some point you'll begin to experience some degree of shift, however small. The Trap Bar is perfect for older lifters because the geometry of the bar helps keep it in line with the center of your body, which helps you counteract any age-related forward shift in your center of gravity.

Dumbbell deadlifts are NOT a good alternative to Trap Bar deadlifts. Heavy dumbbells are too awkward to manage, they rub against your legs when you lift them, and they always pose a risk to your feet and toes. In addition, dumbbells are almost always loaded with smaller plates, which means you have to bend over too low to get into the starting position—and this puts your lower back at risk.

## POWER CLEANS

Provided that you do them in good form, power cleans are one of the most effective exercises for older lifters. Power cleans are an athletic exercise. They develop strength, explosive power, speed, mobility, coordination, neurological efficiency, timing, good balance and over-all athleticism. Remember what I said earlier. You may not be playing sports anymore, but you're still playing the Game of Life. You need to be ready for blocking, tackling and carrying the ball over the goal line.

By the way, power cleans are a terrific leg exercise for older lifters. If you perform your cleans properly, you actually jump with the weight. The jumping motion keeps your legs strong and powerful. There's an old saying about a man being as old as his legs. It's true. And it's one of the big reasons why compound exercises, ground-based movements and athletic-style exercises are so effective for older lifters.

As with your other exercises, good form is critical when you perform power cleans. And again, it's important not to try to train too heavy. If you have too much weight on the bar, you'll try to lift it in bad form. It's much better to go a bit lighter, and to use perfect form, than to go heavier and use bad form and poor lifting technique.

There are plenty of on-line videos showing young lifters (often high school football players) performing power cleans and hang power cleans in absolutely atrocious form. The lift is always followed by cheering and screaming from the other kids, and by WWE-style "tough guy" theatrics from the lifter—and if the coach is there, he throws his clip-board for extra emphasis, jumps up and down and yells louder than any of them. That's fine and good, and perhaps their youthful bodies will hold up to the abuse, but for an older lifter that sort of thing would be suicide. Don't set yourself up for a serious injury by trying to show off, and don't ever try to lift more than you can handle in perfect form. For older lifters, it's not about how much you lift, it's about how much you lift in perfect form.

The biggest problem that older lifters have with the power clean is poor shoulder mobility, which makes it hard to catch the bar in the proper position when the weight is at your shoulders. This is often a problem for lifters who have done plenty of bench pressing. Their shoulders are often extremely tight from all the years of heavy benching. The problem can be corrected, but it takes time and patience, and you have to follow a well-designed stretching program.

Wear lifting shoes for your power cleans. Leave the Chuck Taylors for the guys who do nothing but curls and triceps work.

## POWER SNATCHES

My personal favorite, and an exercise that is infinitely rewarding. The snatch was a favorite exercise of many Golden Age champions, including Steve Stanko, the first man in history to total 1,000 pounds in the three Olympic lifts (back when lifters performed the military press, snatch and clean and jerk in competition). Stanko was a United States National Champion and almost certainly would have been a world and Olympic champion had World War II not intervened. He also won the Mr. America and Mr. Universe contests, and is one of only two men in history (the other being John Grimek), to win the United States Senior National Weightlifting Championship, the Mr. America contest and the Mr. Universe title. Stanko once said, "If I had to do it all over again, snatches are all I would do."

The power snatch has all the benefits of the power clean, but it's an even faster movement. I used to move really fast when I was a high school wrestler, and I want to hold onto some of that speed no matter what my age. That's one reason I enjoy power snatches so much.

You need flexible shoulders to perform power snatches safely and correctly. Don't try to go out and do them without spending some time on flexibility work. You need to lay a proper foundation for power snatches.

As with all other ground-based exercises, lifting shoes are a must for power snatches.

## HIGH PULLS

These are standard movements used by Olympic weightlifters to build extra pulling power for snatches and cleans. They're also excellent exercises for older lifters. In fact, many older lifters who have difficulty in performing power cleans or power snatches due to shoulder flexibility issues or chronic shoulder problems will find that snatch grip and clean grip high pulls are an excellent substitute for power snatches and power cleans.

As with the other exercises, the key is to perform the movement in perfect form—at the right speed—and with the right weight. Going too heavy on high pulls will reduce your results significantly. For best results, use no more than 20 pounds over the weight you could power clean (for clean grip high pulls) or power snatch (for snatch grip high pulls). Too many lifters go too heavy on their high pulls, and end up performing a deadlift followed by an ugly sort of heave at the end of the movement. Don't do that—use a lighter weight and make the movement smooth, explosive and powerful.

A height gauge is an excellent tool to measure the height of your high pulls and to make sure you are performing the movement with plenty of power.

Wear lifting shoes for your high pulls.

## MILITARY PRESSES

In the old days, men trained primarily on overhead lifts, and included plenty of barbell and dumbbell presses, and plenty of heavy jerks, in their training programs. Movements like the floor press and the bench press were strictly secondary exercises until the 1950's, and many men never used them—or used them only rarely. And in those days, it was very rare for a lifter to complain of shoulder problems.

Beginning in the 1950's, lifters went crazy about the bench press. The Weider magazines of the early 1950's proclaimed a "race" to the first 500 pound bench press, and published articles profiling the men who might get there: World and Olympic Games weightlifting champion, John Davis—bodybuilder John McWilliams—bodybuilder and lifter, Marvin Eder—the Canadian Hercules, Doug Hepburn—and bodybuilder Reg Park were all in the running. Doug Hepburn eventually made the first 500 pound bench press in 1954, and Reg Park followed shortly after to become the second man to bench press a quarter of a ton. Bodybuilder and gym owner Vince Gironda supposedly gave Hepburn a special trophy to commemorate his achievement—a strange bit of Iron Game irony, because Gironda never liked the bench press and urged bodybuilders at his gym in North Hollywood, California to perform V-bar dips, ring pushups, ring flies, and other exercises in its place.

In any event, by the mid-1950's, the world was thoroughly, utterly and totally bench press mad—and has remained that way ever since. One result is that many older lifters suffer from sore shoulders caused by years of over-doing it on the bench press. Unlike standing presses, push presses and jerks, which work the entire shoulder girdle, the bench press focuses most of the effort on the front portion of the deltoids. As a result, the bench press can cause muscular imbalances, especially for lifters who do plenty of bench presses and little or no overhead work—and who don't train their upper backs as hard as they train their bench presses.

Old time lifters from the pre-bench era didn't suffer from shoulder problems. They kept their shoulders strong and powerful—and healthy—through years of specialized training on a variety of overhead lifts, using presses, push presses, split jerks and power jerks. You can do the same thing—and you should! You don't necessarily have to perform any jerks—although that's fine if you know how to do them. Standing presses and push presses will do the job just as well. So will heavy dumbbell presses. John Grimek used to do plenty of presses with a pair of 100 pound dumbbells when he was in his 60's—and even into his 70's. That's another example of how a lifetime of heavy overhead lifting can build and maintain strong and healthy shoulders!

Enough with the history lesson. The point is clear. Do plenty of overhead pressing—and do it in military style, not in any sort of slump press or lean-back press. An older lifter should NEVER perform overhead presses with any sort of a lean-back or back-bend. It's far too hard on your spine. Always perform your over-head presses in perfect military style.

## PUSH PRESSES

The push press is a dynamic, explosive movement. It's much more of an athletic exercise than the military press—and that means that it's a very valuable lift for older lifters. Put plenty of time and effort into your push presses. They'll keep your entire shoulder girdle strong, thick and powerful.

Dr. Ken Leistner used to perform push presses in a unique and highly beneficial fashion. He would push press the bar in the conventional fashion, and then fight as hard as possible to slow the descent of the bar as he lowered it to his shoulders. In other words, he'd do a heavy negative-resistance ("eccentric contrac-tion") military press after each push press. Try this sometime. Sets of three are good. The heavy negatives will tire you out very quickly, and you won't be able to lift the bar overhead if you try to perform too many reps.

## JERKS

The jerk is an extremely explosive, athletic exercise. If you know how to perform them, you can generate more power in the jerk than in any other exercise. That's very important when you're trying to preserve explosive power, speed, and coordination.

Be sure to wear lifting shoes when you perform heavy jerks. Your feet take quite a pounding on this movement.

## THE POWER CLEAN AND PRESS

John Grimek once wrote an article where he called the clean and press the best exercise under the sun. He noted that you could get great results by performing an entire workout consisting of nothing but the clean and press. And anyone who has ever tried it will tell you that Grimek was right!

The power clean and push press works just as well, as does the power clean and jerk.

There are many different ways to combine power cleans with your choice of military presses, push presses or jerks. You can perform one clean and one press (or push press or jerk) on each rep. This is tough because you're doing two lifts in each rep, so keep the reps down. Three clean and jerks is really six reps (three reps for cleans and three reps for jerks), four reps is really eight reps, and five reps is really ten reps.

Another option is to do a set of cleans followed by an over-head lift of your choice after the final clean. For example, you might do three power cleans followed by one push press. Or, if you prefer, you could do three power cleans followed by two presses, two push presses or two jerks. There are lots of options and they all will give you a terrific workout.

Some lifters like to do the power clean and press, and as they add weight to the bar, they shift to the push press or the jerk. That works well as long as your skill level in the push press or jerk allows you to perform the movement in perfect form without a series of lighter sets. Personally, I prefer to do clean and press in one workout and clean and jerk in another workout.

## DUMBBELL PRESSES

John Grimek maintained remarkable strength and muscular development to a very advanced age by training on two movements in his fifties, sixties and seventies: the back squat and the standing dumbbell press. Jan Dellinger, the former editor of *Strength & Health* and *Muscular Development,* often saw Grimek performing sets and reps with a pair of 100 pound dumbbells when he was in his sixties—which may well be an all-time world record for a man of Grimek's age and weight.

Dumbbells are made to order for older lifters. For many older lifters, dumbbells are much easier on the shoulders than a barbell. Dumbbells allow you to find the exact groove that works best for you. With dumbbells, you can point your elbows forward, to the sides, or anywhere in-between. You can rotate your hands so your palms are facing away from you (the same as if you were holding onto a barbell), or you can turn them at an angle—or rotate them all the way in so that you perform your presses with your knuckles parallel to one another. You can perform simultaneous dumbbell presses or alternate arm presses.

## COMBINATION EXERCISES

Combining the power clean with an overhead lift is perhaps the best known and most frequently used combination exercise, but there are many others. Examples include power snatch and overhead squat, power clean and front squat, front squat and press, front squat and push press, front squat and jerk, and combinations involving lifts from the floor and lifts from the hang or from boxes.

If you're looking for a super-effective and intense combination, try power cleans followed by front squats, followed by an overhead lift of your choice. That's three moves in one, and it will give you a heck of a workout.

## BENCH PRESS AND INCLINE PRESS

I'm a bit reluctant about including these exercises because so many trainees overdo them, and because ground-based exercises have much greater benefit for older lifters. In addition, many older lifters suffer from shoulder problems that may have been caused by too much bench pressing—or that are exacerbated by bench pressing. On the other hand, bench presses and incline presses will allow you to work your shoulders, triceps and chest without stressing your lower back, and as long as you don't overdo it, that's probably a good thing for an older lifter. Olympic weight-lifting coach Jim Schmitz likes his lifters (including older lifters) to include some bench pressing and incline pressing in their workouts, and that's a pretty good endorsement. Jim Schmitz really knows his stuff.

As with other exercises, the proper technique is very important. In powerlifting competition, you plant your feet firmly on the floor and lay back on the bench with an exaggerated high arch in your back in order to gain a leverage advantage and reduce the distance you have to move the weight. That helps you lift more in competition, but it's awfully tough on your lower back. Older lifters are better off performing incline presses and bench presses with their entire spine flat against the bench. For bench presses, you can put your feet on the bench or even raise them and cross your legs at the ankles to avoid raising your hips when the weight gets heavy.

As an older lifter, you don't need to go super heavy in the bench press. Try to keep your upper body strength in good balance. Don't go crazy on your bench pressing and neglect your overhead lifting. I'd rather see you bench about what you clean and jerk (or a bit more) than bench a ton and skip your overhead lifting. And if you bench more than you squat and deadlift, start wearing a sign that says "Kick me!" Your squat and deadlift deserve way more respect than that.

As I've mentioned before, I have shoulder problems dating back to my high school days, and I had to stop bench pressing in my late thirties. Several years ago, while I was rehabbing a severe shoulder injury (caused by yoga training, of all things), I tried dumbbell bench presses while lying with my shoulders on a heavy-duty stability ball, and it felt okay. Not great, but okay. The stability ball allows me to perform bench presses with an arch in my thoracic spine, and that seems to make all the difference. I've also tried one-arm stability ball bench presses (using one dumbbell at a time), and stability ball bench presses with a barbell. I'm not wild about the movement, but I thought I'd mention it as food for thought. You may want to try it some day. If you do, though, be sure to invest in a really strong, heavy-duty stability ball. You don't want the darn thing to burst when you're performing a bench press! (Note: I've never tried it, but a safer alternative might be to perform barbell or dumbbell bench presses while lying on a large, heavy duty sandbag that allows you to perform the exercise with a thoracic arch.)

## LIFTING FROM BLOCKS

Many older lifters have maintained outstanding levels of strength and power by performing deadlifts, Trap Bar deadlifts, power cleans, power snatches or high pulls from blocks. (Note; when I refer to lifting from blocks, I refer to the plates on the bar being positioned on blocks so the bar is higher at the beginning of the lift than if the plates were on the floor. I am NOT talking about exercises where the lifter stands on a platform to begin the lift from an unusually low position.) Lifting from blocks is often easier on an older lifter's lower back than is lifting from the floor. It's an excellent way to keep on lifting heavy as you grow older. If you don't believe me, ask Dr. Jim Dauer—at age 62, he can perform a Trap Bar deadlift from blocks with 1160 pounds!

# 8

---

# THE ROLE OF
# AUXILIARY EXERCISES

Now don't get me wrong, and don't go out and sell your EZ curl bar on eBay. As long as you're hitting your back and front squats, deadlifts, Trap Bar deadlifts, power cleans, power snatches, and overhead movements, there's nothing wrong with doing biceps or triceps work, or doing some "bodybuilding" exercises if you wish to do so. Isolation exercises can help you recuperate from injuries, and they can help you pump blood into an injured (or merely stiff and sore) body-part—and that can help recovery and recuperation and help to keep you flexible, limber and mobile. Heavy training tends to make an older lifter stiff, sore and inflexible—and anything that can help the recovery and recuperation process is a very good thing. Thus, even if you're a dyed-in-the-wool strength and power guy, as you grow older you may find a place in your program for "bodybuilding" exercises.

The point is, don't over-do it, and don't make it the primary focus of your training. Think of it as auxiliary work, and do it at the end of your workout, after you've done the more important exercises discussed in the previous chapter. Or do it on a separate training day devoted to nothing but auxiliary exercises.

And lest you think I've gone off the deep end in making this suggestion, let me note that the idea originated with none other than Tommy Kono, a man who ranks as one of the greatest Olympic weightlifters of all time. Tommy had a very long competition career (he competed in three different Olympic Games), and he had to make adjustments over the years. As he grew older, the World and Olympic champion and World record holder would include bodybuilding movements as auxiliary exercises in his Olympic lifting workouts. In fact, when he was in his early to mid-thirties (which is "old" for a world-class Olympic lifter) Kono would sometimes do nothing but bodybuilding exercises for two weeks prior to a contest. This helped his body heal from the dents and dings that he had accumulated over the years, and made him hungry to do heavy lifting in the competition. Had Master's lifting been around at the time, and had he decided to compete in Master's competition, Kono probably would have devoted more and more of his training to "bodybuilding" exercises as he moved into his forties, fifties and sixties. So don't dismiss "bodybuilding" as something exclusively for the guys with the bikini briefs and the fake suntans. It has a legitimate place in an older lifter's arsenal of training tools.

And think about this. If you're going to do some "bodybuilding," why not do it in a way that promotes cardiovascular fitness? Use super-sets, tri-sets, compound sets and PHA training. Work fast, and don't spend too much time resting between sets. Make your bodybuilding session a fitness session. It's important for older lifters to maintain a reasonably high level of cardiovascular fitness. Most lifters hate running or "cardio" work, so why not get some cardiovascular training from your weight training workouts?

An easy way to do this is to divide your workouts into one or two heavy sessions where you concentrate on total-body, compound movements and one session where you do nothing but "bodybuilding" work. For example, you might try something like the following:

## Workout A (performed on Tuesday)

1. 10–20 minute warm-up
2. Power clean and press 5 × 5, 5 × 3 or 5/4/3/2/1
3. Back squat or front squat 5 × 3
4. Gut work—1 or 2 sets
5. Neck work with a head-strap—1 or 2 sets
6. Post-workout stretching, hang from bar to decompress spine, etc.

## Workout B (performed on Thursday)

1. 10–20 minute warm-up
2. Trap Bar deadlift 5 × 5, 5 × 3 or 5/4/3/2/1
3. Push press 5 × 3
4. Barbell bent-over rowing 5 × 5
5. Gut work—1 or 2 sets
6. Post-workout stretching, hang from chinning bar, etc.

## *Workout C (performed on Saturday or Sunday)*

1. Front squat 3 × 10–12
   supersetted with
2. Leg curls 3 × 10–12
3. Barbell or dumbbell incline press 3 × 12/10/8
   supersetted with
4. Pull-downs to the chest 3 × 12/10/8
5. Barbell or dumbbell bench press 3 × 12/10/8
   supersetted with
6. Barbell bent-over rowing or seated pulley rowing
   3 × 12/10/8
7. Military press or dumbbell press 3 × 10/8/6
   supersetted with
8. Alternate dumbbell front raise 3 × 10–12
9. Barbell curl 3 × 10/8/6
   supersetted with
10. Close grip bench press 3 × 10/8/6
11. Crunch or bent-legged sit-up 3 × 12–15
    supersetted with
12. Prone hyperextension 3 × 12–15

Note that in the above program, you do NOT go super heavy on your "bodybuilding" day, and you do NOT train to failure. Use weights that are challenging, and make you work with concentration and focus, but don't try to turn it into a strength building session. Your strength and power work comes on the other two days of the week. This one is for fitness, for cardiovascular training, and to get the blood moving through your body. Think of it as "active rest."

As noted above, another option would be to perform your auxiliary exercises after your core strength training movements. For example, you might try the following program:

## Workout A (Tuesday)

1. Warm-up
2. Power snatch 5 × 3, then 3 × 1 (start light and add weight on each set)
3. Front squat 7 × 3 (start light and add eight on each set)
4. Three circuits consisting of the following exercises performed back to back, with no rest between exercises:
    a. Hyperextension 10–12 reps
    b. Alternate front raise 10–12 reps per arm
    c. Hammer curl with dumbbells or reverse curl with barbell 6–8 reps
    d. Close grip bench press 6–8 reps
    e. Hanging knees to chest 10–15 reps
    f. Pull-down to chest 6–8 reps

## Workout B (Thursday)

1. Power clean and press or push press 2 × 5, 2 × 3, 2 × 2, 2 × 1 (start light and add weight on each set)
2. Back squat 5 × 5 or 5 × 3 (start light and add weight on each set)
3. Three circuits consisting of the following exercises performed back to back, with no rest between exercises:
   a. Barbell bent-over rowing 8–10 reps
   b. Alternate dumbbell press 8–10 reps per arm
   c. Dumbbell side bends 10–15 reps per side
   d. EZ Bar curl 6–8 reps
   e. Close grip pushup with your feet on an exercise bench 20–30 reps
   f. Neck exercise with a head-strap 10–12 reps
   g. Standing calf raise or one leg calf raise 15 reps

## Workout C (Saturday or Sunday)

1. Push press, incline press or jerk 5–7 × 3 (start light and add weight on each set)
2. Trap Bar deadlift 5–7 × 5 reps or 5 × 5, 1 × 3, and 1 × 1 (start light and add weight on each set)
3. Three circuits consisting of the following exercises performed back to back, with no rest between exercises:
   a. Front squat 10–12 reps
   b. Dumbbell bench press 10–12 reps
   c. Crunch 12–15 reps
   d. Incline dumbbell curl 8–10 reps
   e. Close grip incline barbell press 8–10 reps
   f. Lateral raise 10–12 reps

Again, on this schedule, you do NOT train with super heavy weights and you do NOT go to failure when doing the "body-building" exercises at the end of each workout. Your strength and power work comes at the beginning of each session. The "body-building" is for overall fitness and cardio training, and to get the blood flowing and help work out any "kinks" from the heavy stuff.

Another way of doing things is to follow the lead of Clarence Bass. While everyone thinks of Clarence as a bodybuilder, he began his journey as an Olympic weightlifter. He didn't begin bodybuilding until he was in his mid-thirties. Later in life, in his sixties, Clarence began to train again on the Olympic lifts. But since he was primarily a bodybuilder, Clarence would divide his program three ways, and take two bodybuilding workouts (using the High Intensity system) followed by a weightlifting workout.

If you're like Clarence, and your primary focus is body-building—or if you simply need more bodybuilding days to help recover from your heavy strength training sessions—you could try the same thing, with two bodybuilding workouts and one weightlifting or strength-oriented workout. (Your bodybuilding workout could be a High Intensity workout similar to those favored by Clarence, or you could do a conventional program as detailed below, and your strength session could focus on athletic type movements or on squats, standing presses and deadlifts or Trap Bar deadlifts, as you prefer.)

You might try something like the following schedule:

## Workout A (Monday)

1. Front squat 3 × 8–10
   tri-setted with
2. Trap Bar deadlift 3 × 8–10
   and
3. Leg curl or hyperextension 3 × 8–10
4. Standing calf raise or one leg calf raise 3 × 15
5. Incline press or incline dumbbell press 3 × 8–10
   supersetted with
8. Barbell bent-over rowing 3 × 8–10
9. Neck work with a head-strap 2–3 × 10–15
10. A non-stop circuit of ten gut exercises of your choice, performed back to back without any rest between exercises.

## Workout B (Wednesday)

1. Alternate dumbbell press 3 × 10–12
   supersetted with
2. One-arm dumbbell rowing or pull-down to the chest 3 × 10–12
3. Alternate front raise 3 × 10–12
   supersetted with
4. Lateral raise 3 × 10–12
5. Alternate dumbbell curl 3 × 8–10
   supersetted with
6. Close grip bench press 3 × 10–12
7. Reverse barbell curl 3 × 10–12
   supersetted with
8. Wrist curl 3 × 12–15
9. Gut work as in Workout A.

## Workout C (Friday or Saturday)

1. Standing press or push press off racks 5 × 5, 1 × 3, 1 × 1 (Start light and add weight on each set.)
2. Back squat or front squat 5–7 progressively heavier sets of 3–5 reps (Start light and add weight on each set.)
3. Deadlift or Trap Bar deadlift 5–7 progressively heavier sets of 3–5 reps (Start light and add weight on each set.)

Again, to make this program work, don't go too heavy on your bodybuilding days. Even when you do strength movements such as the front squat or Trap Bar deadlift, keep the weights under control. Just use enough to break a sweat and get the blood flowing. Save your heavy lifting for your heavy day when you tackle Workout C—and when you do, give it all you've got.

Still another option is an approach similar to that of Tommy Kono when he was in his thirties and alternated periods of strength and power training with lighter periods of pure bodybuilding work.

I know that some readers are going to think, "What's with the bodybuilding stuff and the isolation exercises? I just want to train for strength!"

Hey, don't get me wrong! I'm just as interested in strength and power training as you are. That's been my focus since I started weight training more than forty years ago, and it's my focus today and it's going to be my focus for as long as I live. And you probably feel the very same way.

All I'm suggesting is that for older lifters, a moderate amount of bodybuilding can actually benefit your strength and power training by keeping you well-conditioned and healthy, with good cardiovascular fitness and good mobility. There's many an older lifter who will tell you that the toughest part of the battle is training heavy enough to maintain your strength and power while not making your joints so stiff and sore that you can't train properly for a long time (perhaps a week or more) or without developing chronic soreness, stiffness and inflammation. If lighter exercises and training for a pump can help the recovery process and keep your joints healthy, then they're well worth doing.

But remember—the fake suntan is optional.

# 9

## UNSAFE AT ANY AGE—
## EXERCISES TO AVOID

When I was in junior high school, a man named Arthur Jones invented and marketed something called the Nautilus Pullover Torso machine. You've probably seen photos of the device, and you may even have seen one in action. Heck, you may even have used one "back in the day." The Pullover Torso machine and other Nautilus exercise machines were heavily marketed, and for awhile they were all the rage, first for bodybuilders and powerlifters, then for athletes (especially football players), and then for Mr. and Mrs. John Q. Public.

The Nautilus Pullover Torso machine allowed you to perform a seated pullover with your elbows pressing against pads attached to the movement arm. You began with your arms stretched back behind your head, and pushed forward in a circular movement that ended with your forearms at your sides and your elbows sticking out behind you, right above your hips. The range of motion was enormous, and the machine was marketed as improving your shoulder flexibility and building strength throughout the shoulder's entire range of motion. Supposedly, you would do everything possible to make yourself injury-proof by training your muscles over an extreme range of motion.

It was a nice idea, and it made great advertising copy. But it didn't work. Not for me, at least.

I read about the Nautilus machines in Arthur Jones' articles in *IronMan* magazine, and I began training on the Pullover Torso machine when I was in high school. By the end of my senior year, after just two years of super-shoulder stretches and strengthening on the Pullover Torso machine, my right shoulder was so stiff and sore that I couldn't raise my arm above shoulder level for almost two years. It made it really tough to go out on a date—I couldn't put my right arm around the girl!

That right shoulder has bothered me ever since—and it still bothers me, even today. And so does my left shoulder.

What I didn't realize when I was a teenager was that it's extremely dangerous to stretch any body-part into a position where you're almost popping out of the joint and simultaneously apply force and then resist the force with muscle contraction. That's what the Nautilus Pullover Torso machine made you do, and I paid the price for using it—and I'm still paying the price.

And the crazy part was this. There was no benefit to performing the exercise over so great a range of motion—and especially no benefit to beginning the movement in a fully extended, super-stretched position. It doesn't make you stronger. It doesn't make you more flexible. Instead, it causes micro-trauma to the muscle fibers and connective tissues, and over time, the micro-trauma accumulates and you end up with a severe joint problem.

The same thing happens in many other exercises, including numerous conventional barbell and dumbbell movements. These are exercises you don't want to do. They're unsafe at any age—and for an older lifter, they can be cripplers.

Other exercises are dangerous because they subject the lifter to unnecessary trauma (such as plyometric "depth jumps"), because they put the lifter's spine and lower back at risk (t-bar rowing or Zercher lifts), because the risk of injury is unacceptably high and there are much safer exercises that do the job as well or better (bench squats and one arm barbell presses), or because they're just plain foolish—meaning that they accomplish nothing at all and always present the risk of a crippling injury (performing barbell squats or any other barbell or dumbbell exercise while standing on a stability ball or balance board).

Here's a list of some of the worst offenders:

## BARBELL OR DUMBBELL PULLOVERS

These have the same effect as the Pullover Torso machine. They are of limited value as strength and muscle builders, and they're potential shoulder wreckers.

## BEHIND THE NECK PULL-DOWNS

Awfully hard on the shoulders at both the start and finish of the exercise, and for many lifters, another shoulder wrecker. Perform pull-downs to the chest instead, and resist the temptation to "stretch" your shoulders at the top of the movement. Reduce the range of movement slightly at the top of the movement and you'll save enormous wear and tear on your shoulders.

## BEHIND THE NECK PULL-UPS

Same problems as the behind the neck pull-down. Do pull-ups to the front instead—and don't fully extend your arms and "stretch" your shoulders at the beginning of each rep.

## PRESS BEHIND NECK

A very bad idea for lifters of any age. The press behind neck can cause severe shoulder problems for many men, especially if they try to lower the bar as far as possible. There's just too much stretch on the shoulders when they're in a compromised position. Use dumbbell presses or military presses instead.

And yes, I KNOW that many well-respected lifters and leading writers have promoted the press behind neck for many years. I KNOW the stories about Reg Park ramming up 300 pounds in the exercise back in the 1950's. But I'm telling it like it is—and the press behind neck is a potential shoulder wrecker. And that's especially true for older lifters, who are always going to be tighter and less flexible than younger men.

## THE BRADFORD EXERCISE

In this movement, you alternate military presses and presses behind the neck. The exercise is named after Jim Bradford, an enormously powerful Olympic weightlifter from the 1950's who sported what may have been the most massive shoulder development of any man who ever lived. Bradford was a great lifter, but the exercise bearing his name is potentially dangerous. The military press is a much better, and safer, option.

## DUMBBELL FLYES

The problem here is the same as the barbell or dumbbell pull-over. If you lower the dumbbells too far to your sides at the bottom of the exercise, you place tremendous pressure on your shoulder joints. Do them often enough, and heavy enough, and you're almost guaranteed to have shoulder problems.

## PARALLEL DIPS

Some men can do these without any difficulty at all—but for others, the parallel dip will destroy their shoulders. Why take the chance? There are plenty of other exercises for the pushing muscles of your upper body, and they're much safer.

If you do choose to perform dips, do NOT go too low. The deep stretch at the bottom is the most dangerous part of the movement. Also, be very careful if you perform dips on rings, which are inherently less stable than dipping bars—or if you perform them on V-bars. If you use V-bars and go too far out to increase the stretch, you're just asking for trouble.

## ONE-ARM BARBELL PRESSES OR BARBELL SIDE PRESSES

There's no reason in the world to perform one-arm barbell presses or barbell side presses. Standing barbell presses and push presses are much more effective and much safer. If for any reason you insist on performing one-arm military presses or side presses, do them with a dumbbell or a kettlebell. Using a barbell for one-arm presses of any sort is always dangerous. If the barbell twists out of position, you can severely injure your shoulder.

## BENCH PRESSES WITH A MCDONALD BAR

The McDonald bar is named after Mike McDonald, a bench press champion from the early days of powerlifting. The bar is designed so you can lower your hands far below the height of your chest, thereby giving your chest and shoulder muscles a really good stretch. Of course, the extra stretch with weight on the bar is precisely what will cause micro-trauma leading to injury. Stick to the regular bar for your bench presses.

## DUMBBELL BENCH PRESSES WITH TOO MUCH STRETCH

Same problem as the McDonald bar bench press. If you perform dumbbell bench presses, use the same range of movement as if you were performing barbell bench presses.

## PREACHER BENCH CURLS

Yeah, I know you still remember the photos of Arnold and Larry Scott training their guns on the preacher bench—and I know it was a Vince Gironda special—and I know it's just downright fun to do—but it puts tremendous stress on the inner elbow in the extended position. Use regular barbell or dumbbell curls instead.

## SUPINE DUMBBELL CURLS

These are dumbbell curls where you prop up one end of a flat bench on a six-inch block or box, lie back, and perform dumbbell curls while lying in a supine position. Reg Park supposedly liked doing these, and the rest of us have been trying them ever since. They're not a very good exercise, and they put lots of stress on your shoulders and inner elbows. Use standing barbell curls and dumbbell curls, along with 45 degree incline dumbbell curls.

## ELEVATED STIFF-LEGGED DEADLIFTS

John Grimek and Maurice Jones are two Iron Game legends who performed this exercise with weights as high as 400 pounds for twelve or fifteen reps. I read about that when I was a kid, and promptly began doing stiff-legged deadlifts while standing on an exercise bench. Luckily, I stopped doing them before I caused serious harm. Grimek and Jones were enormously flexible, enormously strong, and had the thickest bones and connective tissue imaginable. For lesser mortals, the stiff-legged deadlift while standing on a bench or block is a very dangerous movement because it imposes tremendous stress on your lower back when it is in a stretched and fully extended position. Stick to bent-legged deadlifts, Trap Bar deadlifts and Olympic lifting exercises (power cleans, power snatches and high pulls) to build your lower back.

## ELEVATED DEADLIFTS

These raise the same concern as the stiff-legged deadlift while standing on a block or bench. There's just too much risk of a lower back injury when your lower back rounds in the bottom position. I know that some powerlifters swear by this exercise, but even if it has the potential to increase your deadlift, any possible benefit is just not worth the risk of a career-ending injury.

### ELEVATED ROWING

Same concerns as stiff-legged deadlifts or bent-legged deadlifts while standing on a block or bench.

### STIFF-LEGGED DEADLIFTS

Some men are built in such a fashion that they can perform heavy stiff-legged deadlifts without any problem. Others are not. I prefer to play it safe, and stick to bent-legged deadlifts, Trap Bar deadlifts, power cleans, power snatches, and high pulls.

87

## T-BAR ROWS

These are almost always performed with too much weight and a rounded back. They can really hurt your lower back.

## THE ZERCHER LIFT

These are a sort of combination squat and deadlift, performed while cradling the barbell in your elbow joints. I don't like these at all. There are much safer exercises for your legs, hips and lower back. The Zercher lift is awfully hard on your lower back, particularly if you allow your body to round forward as you perform the exercise. I know that some powerlifters like the exercise, but again, there are far better and much safer alternatives.

## THE GOOD MORNING EXERCISE

This exercise is performed with the barbell behind your head, as if you were going to do a set of squats—but you bend at the waist and lean forward until your upper back is parallel to the floor, and then reverse the movement and return to the starting position. The exercise can be performed with stiff legs, in which case it is similar to a stiff-legged deadlift, or with your legs slightly bent. In either case, it's always a risky exercise. Again, I'd stick to bent-legged deadlifts, Trap Bar deadlifts, power cleans, power snatches and high pulls.

## THE SEATED GOOD MORNING EXERCISE

This is a good morning exercise performed with a barbell on your shoulders while you are seated on an exercise bench. (You straddle the bench and lean foreword as you perform the movement.)

Some Olympic weighlifters and weightlifting coaches like this exercise. I don't. The risk of injury is too high, and it's not a very good lower back exercise. There are much better and safer alternatives, so why do it?

## TRICEPS EXTENSIONS AND FRENCH PRESSES

These have a well-deserved reputation as elbow-wreckers. It's much better and safer to train your triceps with close grip bench presses (performed with your hands no closer than six inches apart). For variety, perform these on an incline bench.

Note: triceps push-downs on a lat machine or overhead pulley are much easier on the elbows, especially if you use a rope handle to perform them. Close grip bench presses are a better movement, but if you MUST do something extra for your triceps, do push-downs instead of triceps extensions or French presses.

## THE STRADDLE LIFT

This was another favorite exercise of John Grimek, and for that reason alone many men have tried it. It's a squat where you straddle the bar and hold it between your legs, with one hand to the front and one hand behind you. If you have a long torso and short arms, the exercise is impossible unless you really enjoy performing sets and reps with an iron bar crushing your manhood. If you have long arms, you can perform the lift, but you have to twist your spine as you do it, and twisting your spine while performing a heavy squat is a great way to hurt your lower back. Squats, front squats, deadlifts and Trap Bar deadlifts work the legs, hips and lower back much more effectively and in a much safer fashion.

## JUMP SQUATS

These are performed with a barbell on your shoulders or with dumbbells in your hands. Weightlifters sometimes use this exercise to build explosive power, and some men have registered impressive performances. John Davis and John Grimek are both reported to have performed the exercise for sets and reps with weights ranging from 135 to 185 pounds back in the 1930's and 1940's. Harry Paschall also reported that Grimek did jumping split squats with a 135 pound bar on his shoulders—supposedly for 60 reps in exactly 60 seconds, which is an amazing performance. I respect Davis, Grimek, and Paschall enormously, but I still don't like the exercise. It places way too much stress on your body to jump up and down with a heavy barbell on your shoulders, and it's not necessary. You can build plenty of explosive power by performing squats, front squats, power cleans, power snatches and high pulls.

## BOX SQUATS AND BENCH SQUATS

I know that lots of powerlifters like to do box squats or bench squats, but an older lifter should never do them. They put enormous pressure on your spine, and you can train your legs and hips very effectively with other, safer movements. If you want to focus on the bottom position of the squat, use a power rack and perform bottom position squats.

## DECLINE BARBELL OR DUMBBELL PRESSES

Not a bad exercise, but older lifters need to be careful with this movement. There have been cases of lifters having strokes or heart attacks while straining as they perform decline pressing exercises.

## SPRINTS AND HILL SPRINTS

Good for younger men, but not for older lifters. The Achilles tendon is very fragile in older lifters, and sprints and hill sprints can cause enormous problems, particularly if you're not used to running or if you weigh over 200 pounds. So this is one that you probably want to leave to the younger guys. If you rupture an Achilles tendon, you're going to be out of action for a very long time—and you may never make it back.

## PLYOMETRICS AND DEPTH JUMPS

See my comments regarding sprints and hill sprints. We can debate the merits—and the safety—of plyometrics and depth jumps for younger trainees, but for older lifters they're a very bad idea.

## YOGA

One of the worst injuries I ever experienced was a shoulder strain that resulted from a Yoga course I tried at age 49. I ended up with a severely strained shoulder that required over six months of rehab. If you're heavily-muscled and over the age of 40, be very careful before embarking on a Yoga course.

## ANYTHING WHERE YOU STAND ON A STABILITY BALL

I don't even have to explain why this is a bad idea.

## LEG PRESSES ON A VERTICAL LEG PRESS MACHINE

If you go too low, these can place enormous stress on your lower back and spine. Not recommended.

## ANY SORT OF PULLOVER MACHINE

See the introduction to this chapter for the reasons to avoid this one.

## THE PEC-DEC

One of the most useless exercises ever invented—and to top it off, it's bad for the shoulders!

## ROUND BACK SQUATS

Back in the old days of the Iron Game, several writers advocated deep knee bends with a rounded back. Joseph. C. Hise, one of the first men to gain massive amounts of bodyweight on a "breathing squat" program, was a proponent of round back squats, as was gym owner Sig Klein. (I know Klein performed deep knee bends in this style as a young man—because I've seen photos that show him doing it. Perhaps he changed his mind as he grew older.) Don't follow their example. Round back squats are murder on your lower back. Always perform your squats with a flat back.

## SIT-UPS WITH STRAIGHT LEGS

You probably know about this one—it's a certified back breaker. If you perform sit-ups, always do them with your knees bent.

## BENCH PRESSES WITH A THUMBLESS GRIP

These are a truly bad idea. I know that many powerlifters like to bench with a thumbless grip (supposedly to gain a little more pushing power)—but as I write this, the news reports are talking about a college football player who dropped a bar on his throat while doing bench presses. He almost died—and ended up in emergency surgery for over seven hours! Luckily, he was working out with teammates and an assistant strength coach, and so he had immediate medical attention. If he'd been training alone, he would have died before anyone even found him.

I've seen National champions and National record holders in the bench press that used a thumbless grip in National competition—and ended up dropping the bar on their chests! And these were very experienced lifters—champions and record holders—and they had two spotters—and the bar still ended up on their chests. If it can happen to an experienced powerlifting champion with two experienced spotters, it can happen to anyone.

## BENCH PRESSING WITHOUT SAFETY RACKS OR SPOTTERS

See the above points. Do you really want to end up gumming oatmeal for the rest of your life?

## QUARTER SQUATS WITHOUT A POWER RACK

This one should be obvious, but you never know what a lifter will decide to do. None other than three-time Mr. Universe, Reg Park, who may have been the strongest bodybuilder in the world at the peak of his career, almost killed himself doing quarter squats with 1,000 pounds on the bar—using a set of free-standing squat stands and no power rack or safety bars. Park trained early in the morning, when the gym was closed and he wouldn't be interrupted. His training partner was late, so he started lifting on his own.

93

He was doing quarter squats, and he planned to work up to a heavy weight. Everything went fine until his final set with 1,000 pounds. When Park tried to rack the bar after finishing his reps, he found that the weight of the bar had compressed him just enough that he couldn't get it back on the squat stands!

The bar was too heavy to drop behind him, and he couldn't rack it, and he couldn't move. He was stuck—and he'd still be standing there, with half a ton on his shoulders, except his training partner happened to walk in the door that very minute, and helped him get the bar back on the rack.

## JOGGING

This is another one that may work fine for younger lifters—but it's murder for older lifters.

There's a terrific scene in one of John McCallum's *Keys to Progress* articles where Uncle Harry, McCallum's bachelor uncle, is running laps on the college track as half a dozen young women in mini-skirts and tight tops sit and watch and cheer him on as he finishes each lap. Uncle Harry flashes a peace sign as he runs by, and the girls swoon. It's supposed to be the way to stay young (jogging, not the girls).

It makes a great story, and everyone who read it at an impressionable age wanted to grow up and be Uncle Harry.

The problem is—jogging is murder for older lifters, particularly those who weigh over 200 pounds. There's just too much pounding on your knees, hips, feet, ankles and lower back.

If you're a long-time jogger or runner and you want to keep it up—or if you don't weigh that much—and if you're closer to 40 than 50, then feel free to disregard my advice and keep on jogging. But for the rest of you, use your lifting to keep your heart and lungs in good shape—or use a type of cardio training that's easier on your joints than running or jogging.

You can still be like Uncle Harry, girls and all (if you're single)—but leave the jogging to the younger, lighter guys.

## ANY EXERCISE THAT HURTS

This should be obvious, but it needs saying. Lifters are a stubborn breed—and that often goes double for older lifters. As an older lifter, your top priority is staying healthy and injury-free. If you do that, and you train regularly and watch your diet, you'll do fine. But if you train foolishly, you'll probably just get hurt. And when you're older, one injury is all it takes to derail your lifting forever.

So here's a very important rule of thumb—if it hurts, don't do it. I don't care how much you like the exercise—I don't care how important an exercise it is—and I don't care who endorses it. Doesn't matter of it was Paul Anderson's favorite exercise, John Grimek's favorite exercise, Steve Stanko's favorite exercise, Doug Hepburn's favorite exercise, Reg Park's favorite exercise or Arnold's favorite exercise. Doesn't matter if it was endorsed by every writer in the history of the Iron Game. Doesn't matter if it's an exercise that I use or that I endorse in this book. If it hurts, don't do it.

I'm trying to be as frank and candid as possible, so I'll use my own case as an example. I think back squats are a terrific exercise, but I don't do them any more because my shoulders are too banged up to hold the bar in the proper position. So I use front squats instead.

I think bench presses are an excellent exercise for those who can do them—but I can't anymore, because they chew up my shoulders—so I use overhead movements to train my shoulder girdle.

Similarly, you may find that certain exercises hurt more than they help—or that they build strength and muscle, and you enjoy doing them, but they just tear you up too much. If that's the case, with ANY exercise, don't keep on doing it. Drop the exercise, and replace it with something that works the same part of the body in a way that doesn't hurt.

## POWER CLEANS OR SNATCHES IF YOU DO THEM WRONG

I've struggled in writing this book because I prefer to train with athletic style exercises—power snatches, power cleans, push presses, jerks and front squats—and I know that many readers feel the same way. Other readers prefer to train with squats and front squats, military presses and bench presses (or incline presses) and bent-legged deadlifts or Trap Bar deadlifts forming the core of their programs.

If you're an older lifter and you've never done power snatches or power cleans, you're probably better off not doing them at all unless you find a good weightlifting coach to teach you these movements. Trying to train on these exercises when you don't know how to perform them properly is undoubtedly going to lead to disappointment and injuries.

In addition, you should only perform athletic strength training exercises if you are flexible enough to perform them safely. Flexibility and joint mobility is a challenge for any older lifter, and you may find that you're simply too tight and too stiff to perform power snatches and power cleans safely and effectively. If that's the case, bent-legged deadlifts and Trap Bar deadlifts are the way to go—and you'll do just fine on them.

# 10

## HOW HEAVY SHOULD
## YOU TRAIN?

In an earlier chapter, I mentioned an interview that Roger LaPointe conducted with Fred Lowe, one of the top Master's weightlifters in the world. At one point during the interview, LaPointe asked Lowe how heavy he trained when preparing for a major contest, and Lowe replied, "I train differently than a lot of people. I don't use weights that exceed more than 85% of my goal for a couple of singles. Sometimes 90% if I'm feeling really good."

Okay, let's go back and think that through.

Here you have one of the top Master's weightlifters in the world—a former United States Senior National Champion and a three time Olympian—a multi-time National and World champion in Master's competition—and a Master's World record holder in three different weight classes—and when he trains, he rarely exceeds 85% of his top weight—and he only does "a couple of singles" with that weight.

Oh—and for the record—Fred Lowe was 54 years old when this interview was recorded. So it's not like he was THAT old.

While we're thinking about Fred Lowe, let's pick up a copy of Artie Dreschler's magnificent treatise, *The Weightlifting Encyclopedia: A Guide to World Class Performance*. At pages 388–389, Artie summarizes the training program of Mike Huszka, another top lifter in Master's competition. What do we see?

"Huszka does not go above 70% of maximum in the classic lifts during the last two weeks before the competition. In his strength and power exercises, Mike uses between 80% and 90% of his maximum two weeks out of competition, applying 80—100% effort on each lift . . . The week before the competition, weights on the power exercises are reduced to 70% of maximum."

We also see that Huszka does plenty of stretching and mobility exercises not only at the beginning and end of his workout, but in-between sets as well. Apparently, it's a very important part of his training.

And then we see something else.

"It is interesting to note that Tommy Kono has advocated training techniques that are similar to Mike's for older athletes."

Is that so?

We grab a copy of Tommy Kono's terrific book, *Weightlifting, Olympic Style*, scan the table of contents, and find the chapter titled "For Master Lifters." We turn to page 238, and read the following: "It is a well-known fact that as we age we become stiff in our joints, losing much of the flexibility we used to have; therefore, we are not as agile and smooth in our movement."

Hey, that's for sure!

We keep on reading.

"One of the main faults of the older lifter is that they do not work for greater flexibility in their training program. They compound the problem by going heavy in the Olympic lift movements

98

that, at this stage of life, creates greater stiffness in the shoulders and knees."

And that's when Tommy Kono—one of the greatest Olympic weightlifting champions in history—drops the bomb.

"If you ever question or study the outstanding master lifters in training, you'll find that the majority of them, in practicing the Olympic lifts, train with 70 to 80 percent of their best lifts and never really push themselves except in a contest."

As you grow older, says Tommy Kono, you need to concentrate on flexibility, technique, smooth lifting and athleticism. If you go overboard in training for sheer strength, you end up making your joints stiff and tight—and the end result is a less competitive athlete. He may be stronger than he used to be, but he can't demonstrate that strength in competition.

Now, competitive Olympic weightlifting requires explosive power, terrific speed, and plenty of flexibility. And it also requires plenty of strength from head to toe. It's not just "lifting weights"—it's lifting weights in as athletic a manner as possible. If your primary interest is powerlifting, strongman competition, bodybuilding, garage gorilla training, or just staying in great shape, you don't need to worry as much about maintaining speed and flexibility. However, the basic principle that underlies Fred Lowe's training, Mike Huzka's program and Tommy Kono's advice to older weightlifters, is still going to be very important for your training success.

As an older lifter, you need to reassess how heavy you train—and how often you train heavy. In order to continue to make progress, to avoid injuries and to enjoy your training, you need to do most of your training in the 70–80% zone. You need to do some training in the 80–90% range, and every once in awhile you need to go up to 95% or even 100%. But the majority of your training should be in the 70–80% range.

If you train heavier than this, you offset any gains in strength and muscular development by overworking your joints, becoming stiff and tight, and setting yourself up for an injury.

The appropriate training range will shift as you grow older. Simply put, the younger you are, the more often you can perform lifts in the 90–100% range, and the more benefit you get from heavy training. As you grow older, you start to do better with lighter weights relative to your one rep max. The difference will start to become noticeable sometime after age 40 for most lifters, and by age 50 it will be very important to avoid going too heavy too often. After age 50, training in the 70–80% zone will be one of the best things you can do for your body.

Now, I know what some of you are thinking. You're thinking I'm crazy. You're thinking about John Grimek doing 400 pound squats and 100 pound dumbbell presses into his sixties—and you're thinking about Karl Norberg bench pressing huge weights in his sixties and seventies—and you're thinking about other older lifters who have posted big numbers at an advanced age—and you're thinking that you're going to do the same.

Trust me, I know how you feel. For a long time, I felt the same way, and I trained hard and heavy every time I touched a barbell, and for a long time, it was all good. But that was then, and this is now. Today, I'm a 52-year old grandfather. That may not sound very old to those of you in your sixties or seventies, but the fact of the matter is, there aren't many guys my age who still train with weights, and there are very few of them who train year round in an unheated, un-air conditioned garage, and even fewer who train with front squats, standing presses, push presses, jerks, power cleans, power snatches, Trap Bar deadlifts and similar movements. If you're my age or older and you're still doing those things, you're doing pretty darn good.

What becomes important at this stage of your career is to keep on doing what you're doing. You want to train regularly and consistently for the rest of your life—and you can't do that if you hurt yourself—and if you keep on lifting heavy weights all the time, or if you go too heavy too often, you're going to hurt yourself.

As an older lifter, you need to get away from the idea of lifting gigantic, massive, superhuman, heroic, mind-boggling, enormous weights all the time in all of your different exercises. You don't need to do that. Instead, you need to train regularly and consistently—and you need to perform each rep that you do in perfect form—and you need to concentrate on smooth, precise, powerful lifting.

To summarize, as an older lifter, here are ten rules to lift by—and to live by:

1. No more of those slow, grinding super-heavy reps.
2. Perform every rep in every workout in perfect form.
3. Own every rep you do.
4. Lift the weight with strength and muscle power, not with a super psyche.
5. Train heavy enough to stimulate gains in strength and muscle without putting your body at risk.
6. If you train too heavy, all you do is make yourself stiff, sore and slow.
7. Train for explosive power, not for sheer strength.
8. How you lift is more important than how much you lift.
9. It's far better to undertrain than overtrain.
10. If it feels heavy, leave it for another day.

In the long run, you'll do far better this way—and for an older lifter, the long run is what it's all about.

# 11

---

# SIMPLE CYCLING PROGRAMS
# FOR OLDER LIFTERS

When I was younger, I trained heavy pretty much all the time. And that worked fine. But as I've grown older, I've changed my approach to things. As I noted in the previous chapter, I've found that as you grow older, you can only train in the 90–100% range once in awhile. I've also found that one of the most important keys to training success is to avoid overtraining, to avoid getting too sore and stiff from your workouts, and to avoid injury. Cycling is a way to help control your training to achieve all of these goals— and that's why I follow simple cycling programs, and why you should do the same thing.

Let me emphasize, though, that I follow a SIMPLE cycling system. I can't stand the long, complicated programs that read like an advanced equation in nuclear physics. When I say "simple" I mean it.

I also don't like long cycles. I prefer four-week cycles. At the end of four weeks, I evaluate my program and make any necessary changes. For an older lifter, changing things around is a good idea. It helps keep you fresh and motivated, and it helps avoid the risk of a nagging injury that might build up over time if you keep hitting the same exercises, sets and reps for a long stretch of time.

If you've trained for a long period of time and you've paid attention to things, you probably have a good idea what sort of cycle works best for you. Cycles are individual things, and if you know from experience that you do best on a six week cycle (or any other number of weeks), then plan a training cycle that matches the number of weeks that works for you. As I said, four weeks works best for me, but that doesn't mean it would work best for you.

In any event, here's an example of a basic cycling program for a lifter who trains three times a week, using three different workouts. It's based on an article by Olympic weightlifting coach Jim Schmitz. The article was entitled "5–4–3–2–1 Done!" and it appeared in the March, 2000 issue of *Milo*. (Good article—go back and read it, and if you don't have a copy of that issue of *Milo*, order it from IronMind.) It's a very basic 70/80/90/95–100% cycling program. (Jim suggested 70/80/90/100% weights, but I've adjusted it a little. See my comments below for percentages for the fourth week of the cycle.) You train on a four-week cycle, and then you start over again and perform a second four-week cycle beginning with 70% weights. In each workout during the first cycle, you perform fives, threes and singles.

In week one, your top single will be 70% of your one rep max. In week two, you use 80% of your one rep max. In week three, you go up to 90% of your one rep max. In week four, you hit 95% of your one rep max. Then you start over again at 70% the next week, and build back up over a four-week period. Your fives and triples follow a similar pattern, i.e., you train with approximately 70% of your top weight for five reps in week one and gradually increase the weight through the course of the cycle.

In your second cycle, you use 70% of your one rep max as

your top weight in week one, 80% in week two, 90% in week three, and 100 percent in week four. Thus, over the course of two four-week training cycles, you have one 95% week and one 100% week. This can be adjusted based on your age. Lifters in their forties may be able to hit 100% of their max in the fourth week of each training cycle, while lifters in their fifties may do best by hitting 95% at the end of the first four-week cycle and 100% at the end of the second four-week cycle, and lifters in their 60's may do best by hitting 100% only after their third (or fourth) four-week cycle. In other words, a lifter in his sixties might do two or three cycles where he finishes with a 90% week, followed by one cycle where he finishes with a 100% week.

In addition, note that you don't have to hit the same percentages in all of your exercises, particularly in week four. Instead, you might do better by going into 95% or 100% territory for a few selected movements, and keeping the others at 90%. Thus, if your primary focus is Olympic weightlifting, you might shoot for 100% lifts in the power snatch, power clean and jerk, and stay at 90% weights for your squats, high pulls, and other exercises. You don't have to use maximum weights in all movements in week four, and you might very well do better by holding back a bit on some of your supplemental movements. For example, if you push your back and front squats to 100% and end up with sore, stiff knees, you might not be able to hit 100% in your power cleans and power snatches. Or you may find that you can hit 100% in your back squats OR your deadlifts in your fourth week—but not in both movements.

In the following example, we'll assume we have a lifter in his early fifties who enjoys training with Olympic style movements. In his first four-week cycle, he's going to shoot for 95% in week four for power cleans, power snatches, and jerks, and hit 90% in his other exercises. In his second four-week cycle, he's going to change his exercises a bit, mix up his sets and reps, and work up to 100% on his target movements in the fourth week. Note how the lifter gradually increases the intensity of his training (measured by average weight per rep) by reducing reps in weeks three and four of the second cycle.

## *Cycle One*

### WEEK ONE—70% ON ALL EXERCISES

*Workout A*

1. Power snatch 2 × 5, 2 × 3, 3 × 1 (add weight on each set)
2. Snatch grip high pull 3 × 3 (use your first 1-rep power snatch weight)
3. Back squat or front squat 2 × 5, 2 × 3, 3 × 1 (add weight on each set)
4. Gut work

*Workout B*

1. Power clean 2 × 5, 2 × 3, 3 × 1 (add weight on each set)
2. Clean grip high pull 3 × 3 (use your first 1-rep power clean weight)
3. Incline press 5 × 5 (add weight on each set)
4. Neck work with head-strap 2–3 × 10–12 (add weight on each set)
5. Gut work

## Workout C

1. Push press 2 × 5, 2 × 3, 3 × 1 (add weight on each set)
2. Clean grip high pull from blocks 5 × 3 (add weight on each set)
3. Prone hyperextension 3 × 10–12 (no weight)
4. Gut work

### WEEK TWO—80% ON ALL EXERCISES

## Workout A

1. Power snatch 2 × 5, 2 × 3, 3 × 1 (add weight on each set)
2. Snatch grip high pull 3 × 3 (use your first 1-rep power snatch weight)
3. Back squat or front squat 2 × 5, 2 × 3, 3 × 1 (add weight on each set)
4. Gut work

## Workout B

1. Power clean 2 × 5, 2 × 3, 3 × 1 (add weight on each set)
2. Clean grip high pull 3 × 3 (use your first 1-rep power clean weight)
3. Incline press 5 × 5 (add weight on each set)
4. Neck work with head-strap 2–3 × 10–12 (add weight on each set)
5. Gut work

## Workout C

1. Push press 2 × 5, 2 × 3, 3 × 1 (add weight on each set)
2. Clean grip high pull from blocks 5 × 3 (add weight on each set)
3. Prone hyperextension 3 × 10–12 (no weight)
4. Gut work

### WEEK THREE—90% ON ALL EXERCISES

## Workout A

1. Power snatch 2 × 5, 2 × 3, 3 × 1 (add weight on each set)
2. Snatch grip high pull 3 × 3 (use your first 1-rep power snatch weight)
3. Back squat or front squat 2 × 5, 2 × 3, 3 × 1 (add weight on each set)
4. Gut work

## Workout B

1. Power clean 2 × 5, 2 × 3, 3 × 1 (add weight on each set)
2. Clean grip high pull 3 × 3 (use your first 1-rep power clean weight)
3. Incline press 5 × 5 (add weight on each set)
4. Neck work with head-strap 2–3 × 10–12 (add weight on each set)
5. Gut work

## Workout C

1. Push press 2 × 5, 2 × 3, 3 × 1 (add weight on each set)
2. Clean grip high pull from blocks 5 × 3 (add weight on each set)
3. Prone hyperextension 3 × 10–12 (no weight)
4. Gut work

**WEEK FOUR—95% ON SELECTED EXERCISES, 90% ON ALL OTHERS**

## Workout A

1. Power snatch 2 × 5, 2 × 3, 3 × 1 (add weight on each set) (95%)
2. Snatch grip high pull 3 × 3 (use your first 1-rep power snatch weight) (90%)
3. Back squat or front squat 2 × 5, 2 × 3, 3 × 1 (add weight on each set) (90%)
4. Gut work

## Workout B

1. Power clean 2 × 5, 2 × 3, 3 × 1 (add weight on each set) (95%)
2. Clean grip high pull 3 × 3 (use your first 1-rep power clean weight) (90%)
3. Incline press 5 × 5 (add weight on each set) (90%)
4. Neck work with head-strap 2–3 × 10–12 (add weight on each set)
5. Gut work

## Workout C

1. Push press 2 × 5, 2 × 3, 3 × 1 (add weight on each set) (95%)
2. Clean grip high pull from blocks 5 × 3 (add weight on each set) (90%)
3. Prone hyperextension 3 × 10–12 (no weight)
4. Gut work

## Cycle Two

### WEEK ONE—70% ON ALL EXERCISES

## Workout A

1. Power snatch 7 × 3 (add weight on each set)
2. Snatch grip high pull from blocks 3 × 3 (use your top 3-rep power snatch weight)
3. Back squat 5 × 3 (add weight on each set)
4. Gut work

## Workout B

1. Power clean 7 × 3 (add weight on each set)
2. Clean grip high pull from blocks 3 × 3 (use your top 3-rep power clean weight)
3. Incline press 5 × 3 (add weight on each set)
4. Neck work with head-strap 2–3 × 10–12 (add weight on each set)
5. Gut work

## *Workout C*

1. Jerk 7 × 2 (add weight on each set)
2. Front squat 5 × 3 (add weight on each set)
3. Prone hyperextension 3 × 10–12 (no weight)
4. Gut work

### WEEK TWO—80% ON ALL EXERCISES

## *Workout A*

1. Power snatch 5 × 3, then 2 × 2 and 1 × 1 (add weight on each set)
2. Snatch grip high pull from blocks 3 × 3 (use your top 3-rep power snatch weight)
3. Back squat 5 × 3 (add weight on each set)
4. Gut work

## *Workout B*

1. Power clean 5 × 3, then 2 × 2 and 1 × 1 (add weight on each set)
2. Clean grip high pull from blocks 3 × 3 (use your top 3-rep power clean weight)
3. Incline press 5 × 3 (add weight on each set)
4. Neck work with head-strap 2–3 × 10–12 (add weight on each set)
5. Gut work

## Workout C

1. Jerk 5 × 2, then 3 × 1 (add weight on each set)
2. Front squat 5 × 3 (add weight on each set)
3. Prone hyperextension 3 × 10–12 (no weight)
4. Gut work

### WEEK THREE—90% ON ALL EXERCISES

## Workout A

1. Power snatch 4 × 3, then 3 × 2 and 2 × 1 (add weight on each set)
2. Snatch grip high pull from blocks 3 × 2 (use your first 2-rep power snatch weight)
3. Back squat 6 × 2 (add weight on each set)
4. Gut work

## Workout B

1. Power clean 4 × 3, then 3 × 2 and 2 × 1 (add weight on each set)
2. Clean grip high pull from blocks 3 × 3 (use your first 2-rep power clean weight)
3. Incline press 6 × 2 (add weight on each set)
4. Neck work with head-strap 2–3 × 10–12 (add weight on each set)
5. Gut work

## Workout C

1. Jerk 4 × 2, then 4 × 1 (add weight on each set)
2. Front squat 6 × 2 (add weight on each set)
3. Prone hyperextension 3 × 10–12 (no weight)
4. Gut work

### WEEK FOUR—100% ON SELECTED EXERCISES, 90% ON ALL OTHERS

## Workout A

1. Power snatch 3 × 3, then 2 × 2 and 3 × 1 (add weight on each set) (100%)
2. Snatch grip high pull from blocks 3 × 2 (use your first 1-rep power snatch weight) (90%)
3. Back squat 6 × 2 (add weight on each set) (90%)
4. Gut work

## Workout B

1. Power clean 3 × 3, then 2 × 2 and 3 × 1 (add weight on each set) (100%)
2. Clean grip high pull from blocks 3 × 3 (use your first 1-rep power clean weight) (90%)
3. Incline press 6 × 2 (add weight on each set) (90%)
4. Neck work with head-strap 2–3 × 10–12 (add weight on each set)
5. Gut work

## Workout C

1. Jerk 3 × 2, then 6 × 1 (add weight on each set) (100%)
2. Front squat 6 × 2 (add weight on each set) (90%)
3. Prone hyperextension 3 × 10–12 (no weight)
4. Gut work

For a lifter who trains with back squats, Trap Bar deadlifts, overhead presses, bench presses and auxiliary movements, here's an example of how two four-week training cycles might look. In this case, we'll assume the lifter is in his mid-forties, and can hit 100% of his max in week four of both cycles. Note how the lifter uses different variations of the 5 × 5 system as he moves through the first four-week cycle, and how he drops to lower reps on his primary movements for his second cycle in order to increase the overall intensity of his program.

## Cycle One

### WEEK ONE—70%

## Workout A

1. Bench press 5 × 5 (two progressively heavier sets and three sets with your working weight)
2. Barbell bent-over rowing or pull-down to the chest 5 × 5 (two progressively heavier sets and three sets with your working weight)
3. Incline press 5 × 5 (two progressively heavier sets and three sets with your working weight)
4. Incline dumbbell curl 3 × 12/10/8 (same weight on each set)
5. Gut work

## Workout B

1. Standing press 5 × 5 (two progressively heavier sets and three sets with your working weight)
2. Alternate front raise 3 × 12/10/8 (same weight on each set)
3. Trap Bar deadlift 5 × 5 (two progressively heavier sets and three sets with your working weight)
4. Neck work with head-strap 2–3 × 10–15
5. Gut work

## Workout C

1. Back squat 5 × 5 (two progressively heavier sets and three sets with your working weight)
2. Close grip bench press 5 × 5 (two progressively heavier sets and three sets with your working weight)
3. Barbell curl, EZ Bar curl or reverse curl 5 × 5 (two progressively heavier sets and three sets with your working weight)
4. Gut work

## WEEK TWO—80%

### *Workout A*

1. Bench press 5 × 5 (three progressively heavier sets and two sets with your working weight)
2. Barbell bent-over rowing or pull-down to the chest 5 × 5 (three progressively heavier sets and two sets with your working weight)
3. Incline press 5 × 5 (three progressively heavier sets and two sets with your working weight)
4. Incline dumbbell curl 3 × 10/8/6 (same weight on each set)
5. Gut work

### *Workout B*

1. Standing press 5 × 5 (three progressively heavier sets and two sets with your working weight)
2. Alternate front raise 3 × 12/10/8 (same weight on each set)
3. Trap Bar deadlift 5 × 5 (three progressively heavier sets and two sets with your working weight)
4. Neck work with head-strap 2–3 × 10–15
5. Gut work

## Workout C

1. Back squat 5 × 5 (three progressively heavier sets and two sets with your working weight)
2. Close grip bench press 5 × 5 (three progressively heavier sets and two sets with your working weight)
3. Barbell curl, EZ Bar curl or reverse curl 5 × 5 (three progressively heavier sets and two sets with your working weight)
4. Gut work

**WEEK THREE—90%**

## Workout A

1. Bench press 5 × 5 (four progressively heavier sets and one set with your working weight)
2. Barbell bent-over rowing or pull-down to the chest 5 × 5 (four progressively heavier sets and one set with your working weight)
3. Incline press 5 × 5 (four progressively heavier sets and one set with your working weight)
4. Incline dumbbell curl 3 × 8 (same weight on each set)
5. Gut work

## Workout B

1. Standing press 5 × 5 (four progressively heavier sets and one set with your working weight)
2. Alternate front raise 3 × 10 (same weight on each set)
3. Trap Bar deadlift 5 × 5 (four progressively heavier sets and one set with your working weight)
4. Neck work with head-strap 2–3 × 10–15
5. Gut work

## Workout C

1. Back squat 5 × 5 (four progressively heavier sets and one set with your working weight)
2. Close grip bench press 5 × 5 (four progressively heavier sets and one set with your working weight)
3. Barbell curl, EZ Bar curl or reverse curl 5 × 5 (four progressively heavier sets and one set with your working weight)
4. Gut work

## Workout A

1. Bench press 5 × 5 (four progressively heavier sets and one set with your working weight) (100%)
2. Barbell bent-over rowing or pull-downs to the chest 5 × 5 (four progressively heavier sets and one set with your working weight) (95%)
3. Incline press 5 × 5 (four progressively heavier sets and one set with your working weight) (95%)
4. Incline dumbbell curl 3 × 6 (same weight on each set) (95%)
5. Gut work

## Workout B

1. Standing press 5 × 5 (four progressively heavier sets and one set with your working weight) (100%)
2. Alternate front raise 3 × 8 (same weight on each set) (95%)
3. Trap Bar deadlift 5 × 5 (four progressively heavier sets and one set with your working weight) (100%)
4. Neck work with head-strap 2–3 × 10–15
5. Gut work

## Workout C

1. Back squat 5 × 5 (four progressively heavier sets and one set with your working weight) (100%)
2. Close grip bench press 5 × 5 (four progressively heavier sets and one set with your working weight) (95%)
3. Barbell curl, EZ Bar curl or reverse curl 5 × 5 (four progressively heavier sets and one set with your working weight) (95%)
4. Gut work

## Cycle Two

### WEEK ONE—70%

## Workout A

1. Bench press 5 × 5, 1 × 3, 1 × 1 (two progressively heavier sets and three sets with your working weight on 5 × 5, add weight and do 1 × 3, add weight and do 1 × 1)
2. Barbell bent-over rowing or pull-down to the chest 5 × 5 (two progressively heavier sets and three sets with your working weight)
3. Incline press 5 × 5 (two progressively heavier sets and three sets with your working weight)
4. Hammer curl with dumbbells or Log Bar 3 × 10/8/6 (same weight on each set)
5. Gut work

## Workout B

1. Standing press 5 × 5, 1 × 3, 1 × 1 (two progressively heavier sets and three sets with your working weight on 5 × 5, add weight and do 1 × 3, add weight and do 1 × 1)
2. One-arm lateral raise 3 × 12/10/8 per arm (same weight on each set)
3. Trap Bar deadlift 5 × 5, 1 × 3, 1 × 1 (two progressively heavier sets and three sets with your working weight on 5 × 5, add weight and do 1 × 3, add weight and do 1 × 1)
4. Neck work with head-strap 2–3 × 10–15
5. Gut work

## Workout C

1. Back squat 5 × 5, 1 × 3, 1 × 1 (two progressively heavier sets and three sets with your working weight on 5 × 5, add weight and do 1 × 3, add weight and do 1 × 1)
2. Close grip bench press 5 × 5 (two progressively heavier sets and three sets with your working weight)
3. Barbell curl, EZ Bar curl or reverse curl 5 × 5 (two progressively heavier sets and three sets with your working weight)
4. Gut work

## Week Two—80%

### Workout A

1. Bench press 5 × 5, 2 × 3, 2 × 1 (three progressively heavier sets and two sets with your working weight on 5 × 5, add weight and do 2 × 3, add weight and do 2 × 1)
2. Barbell bent-over rowing or pull-down to the chest 5 × 5 (three progressively heavier sets and two sets with your working weight)
3. Incline press 5 × 5, 2 × 3 (three progressively heavier sets and two sets with your working weight on 5 × 5, add weight and do 2 × 3)
4. Hammer curl with dumbbells or Log Bar 4 × 12/10/9/8 (same weight on each set)
5. Gut work

### Workout B

1. Standing press 5 × 5, 2 × 3, 2 × 1 (three progressively heavier sets and two sets with your working weight on 5 × 5, add weight and do 2 × 3, add weight and do 2 × 1)
2. One-arm lateral raise 3 × 12/10/8 each arm (same weight on each set)
3. Trap Bar deadlift 5 × 5, 2 × 2, 2 × 1 (three progressively heavier sets and two sets with your working weight on 5 × 5, add weight and do 2 × 3, add weight and do 2 × 1)
4. Neck work with head-strap 2–3 × 10–15
5. Gut work

## Workout C

1. Back squat 5 × 5, 2 × 3, 2 × 1 (three progressively heavier sets and two sets with your working weight on 5 × 5, add weight and do 2 × 3, add weight and do 2 × 1)
2. Close grip bench press 5 × 5 (three progressively heavier sets and two sets with your working weight)
3. Barbell curl, EZ Bar curl, or reverse curl 5 × 5 (four progressively heavier sets and one set with your working weight)
4. Gut work

### WEEK THREE—90%

## Workout A

1. Bench press 5 × 3, 3 × 1 (five progressively heavier sets of 3 reps, and three progressively heavier singles)
2. Barbell bent-over rowing or pull-down to the chest 5 × 5 (four progressively heavier sets and one set with your working weight)
3. Incline press 5 × 3 (four progressively heavier sets and one set with your working weight)
4. Hammer curl with dumbbells or Log Bar 3 × 8 (same weight on each set)
5. Gut work

## Workout B

1. Standing press 5 × 3, 3 × 1 (four progressively heavier sets of 3 reps, and three progressively heavier singles)
2. One-arm lateral raise 3 × 10 (same weight on each set)
3. Trap Bar deadlift 5 × 3, 3 × 1 (four progressively heavier sets of 3 reps, and three progressively heavier singles)
4. Neck work with head-strap 2–3 × 10–15
5. Gut work

## Workout C

1. Back squat 5 × 3, 3 × 1 (five progressively heavier sets of 3 reps, and three progressively heavier singles)
2. Close grip bench press 5 × 5 (four progressively heavier sets and one set with your working weight)
3. Barbell curl, EZ Bar curl or reverse curl 5 × 5 (four progressively heavier sets and one set with your working weight)
4. Gut work

### WEEK FOUR—100% ON SELECTED EXERCISES, 95% ON ALL OTHERS

## *Workout A*

1. Bench press 3 × 3, 4 × 1 (three progressively heavier sets of 3 reps, and four progressively heavier singles) (100%)
2. Barbell bent-over rowing or pull-down to the chest 5 × 5 (four progressively heavier sets and one set with your working weight) (95%)
3. Incline press 5 × 3 (four progressively heavier sets and one set with your working weight) (95%)
4. Hammer curl with dumbbells or Log Bar 3 × 6 (same weight on each set) (95%)
5. Gut work

## *Workout B*

1. Standing press 3 × 3, 4 × 1 (three progressively heavier sets of 3 reps, and four progressively heavier singles) (100%)
2. One-arm lateral raise 3 × 10 (same weight on each set) (95%)
3. Trap Bar deadlift 4 × 3, 4 × 1 (four progressively heavier sets of 3 reps, and four progressively heavier singles) (100%)
4. Neck work with head-strap 2–3 × 10–15
5. Gut work

## Workout C

1. Back squat 4 × 3, 4 × 1 (four progressively heavier sets of 3 reps, and four progressively heavier singles) (100%)
2. Close grip bench press 5 × 5 (four progressively heavier sets and one set with your working weight) (95%)
3. Barbell curl, EZ Bar curl or reverse curl 5 × 5 (four progressively heavier sets and one set with your working weight) (95%)
4. Gut work

Before closing, let me add several additional comments about cycling programs. First of all, older lifters have job responsibilities, social obligations, and family commitments that sometimes make it impossible to take a scheduled workout—or that make it impossible to train for an entire week or longer. As an older lifter, what do you do if something happens that causes you to miss a couple of workouts—or perhaps even an entire week of training? Do you continue the cycle where you left off, jump ahead to where you would have been, or go back and start over?

Your best bet is probably to go back and start over at the beginning of the cycle. Training cycles are all about gathering momentum, and if something knocks you off track, you need to go back and start over from the beginning just to get the momentum going. I know that's not fun, and it's not something that's easy to do, but it's the sensible thing to do—and in the long run, it's the most productive thing to do.

Another option would be to drop back one week in the cycle and build back up from there. So if you get knocked off track in week three of your cycle, try dropping back and repeating the week two program, followed by the week three program, and then the week four program.

A second point concerns longer cycles and the idea of hard and easy weeks. If you prefer to train on longer cycles, such as a ten, twelve, or sixteen-week cycle, it's a good idea to build in some easy weeks. It's very difficult for your mind and body if you increase the weight on the bar, volume and intensity for a steady period of ten or more weeks. For most older lifters, it works much better to schedule a couple of light weeks to give the mind and body a bit of a break.

For example, if you wanted to perform a sixteen-week cycle, you might try the following:

Week 1—70%
Week 2—75%
Week 3—80%
Week 4—85%
Week 5—85%
Week 6—75%
Week 7—80%
Week 8—85%
Week 9—90%
Week 10—95%
Week 11—80%
Week 12—85%
Week 13—90%
Week 14—90%
Week 15—95%
Week 16—100%

Third—and this point is very important—an older lifter needs to define his one rep max a little differently than a younger lifter.

For a younger lifter, a one rep max is your current best. It may be very tough but smooth and steady all the way—or it may be a gut-busting, eye-popping, ugly as sin, slow, grinding, agonizing effort that barely would have managed two white lights in competition. A lift that looks sort of like Sylvester Stallone's face at the end of any of the *Rocky* movies. Even if he wins, he looks like he's been through a war.

What's more, for a younger lifter the one rep max is a lift where you are totally psyched up and the adrenaline is pumping like crazy. It's a lift you would miss as often as you'd make it—and a lift that you may have hit on your lucky day, when your bio-rhythms were perfect, and when the stars aligned exactly right for you. In other words, it's a lift that is definitely not a sure thing.

An older lifter needs a different definition of his one rep max. For an older lifter, your one rep max should be the top weight that you can handle for one rep in a smooth, steady lift performed in letter perfect form, with razor sharp technique and total control. It's a lift you focus for, concentrate on, and get really serious about, but it's not a lift where you go into Super Psyche mode. It's not your all time best ever lift, and it's not a lift you make only on a good day. It's a lift you own.

If you base your one rep max on the younger lifter's definition of his one rep max, you'll end up training too hard and too heavy throughout your cycle—and probably not making your 100% lift at the end of your cycle—and that's not a good thing. Base your percentages on the older lifter's definition of his one rep max, and you'll do fine.

Finally, pay close attention to your body and how it responds to different exercises and different percentages all through your training cycle. Learn where you get the most out of your workouts. If you do best in the 80% range, then consider a training cycle where you spend most of your time at that range. And remember, different exercises will probably work best at different percentages of your one rep max. You might do best in the 70–80% range on some movements, while using 80–90% on others. And your "best" percentages for different exercises may change as you grow older. So pay attention, keep your eyes open, and keep careful notes in your training journal.

# 12

## SETS, REPS, WEIGHT, AND THE
## STABILIZING PRINCIPLE

When I look back over the last ten or fifteen years of my training—from my late 30's to my early 50's—I see a lot of things that I did that were "right"—and several things I did that were "wrong." The "right" things included building a platform for performing Olympic weightlifting exercises, investing in an Eleiko barbell and rubber bumper plates, emphasizing athletic style strength training, starting to wear Olympic lifting shoes, using knee sleeves, doing plenty of Trap Bar deadlifts, developing a diet and nutrition plan that works really well for me, using fish oil, eliminating certain exercises that caused problems for me, learning the ins and outs of effective ab training for an older lifter, successfully rehabilitating a frozen left shoulder without surgery, and even a long period of bodyweight training that served as a sort of total body rehabilitation program after a lifetime of heavy training.

The "wrong" things included hill sprints, which almost crippled me—yoga, which caused the frozen shoulder—the wrong kind of ab training, which caused severe lower back spasms—and some nutritional experiments that amounted to dietary disasters.

But the "worst" thing I did was to train too heavy, too often—meaning that I used weights that were too close to my one rep maximum way too often, and I performed way too many reps with them. I got away with it when I was in my early forties, but as time passed, it became more and more of a problem—and today, in my early fifties, I have to consciously hold back and avoid the temptation of training with too much weight on the bar. I have to use set/rep schemes and cycling programs to keep myself from training too heavy. If I don't, I end up going back to my old habits, piling the weight onto the bar, and taking workouts that make my joints ache and protest for days afterward.

I share this because there's a very good chance that you're doing the very same thing. Most older lifters do. In fact, as an older lifter, it's almost easier to train too heavy than it is to train too light. And it's far more common among serious lifters.

The reason is simple. After a long period of serious lifting in your teens, twenties, and thirties, you've developed tremendous muscular strength, thickened and strengthened tendons, ligaments and bone structure, and developed the technical skill and mental attitude that allows you to lift extremely heavy weights. You've also developed the mindset that you MUST train heavy to get good results, and you've developed the belief that a workout doesn't count (or won't be effective) unless you go 100% in weight, reps, and intensity. You view certain weights as "heavy" and certain weights as "light"—and you tend to forget that the weights you view as "light" are three or four times what an average, untrained man could lift.

I remember a time when I was 47 years old, and was training on military presses out in the garage. I had 230 or 240 pounds on the bar, and was performing a series of ten singles with it. I viewed the weight as "light"—meaning, "light enough to perform ten singles"—because I used to do power clean and press with 265 or 270 pounds pretty regularly just five years earlier—and at the same time, I had done a push press with 320 pounds. In comparison, 240 was "light."

My teenage stepson and several of his friends stopped by and asked how much I was lifting.

I told them.

One of them was impressed, one of them thought it was nothing at all because he knew about "a guy in the Olympics who bench pressed 1,000 pounds," and the others didn't really care because they wanted to go to the coffee shop and check out the girls.

"Can I try to lift it?" asked one of them.

"Not by yourself—but two of you can try."

"How do we do that?"

"Well—you grab it here, at this end, and he can grab it here, at the other end—and see if you can lift it overhead."

Two of them tried.

The bar didn't budge.

We added a third kid, positioned in the center of the bar.

They tried and missed.

Caught their collective breath and tried again—and made it, in a ragged sort of ugly, push, press and heave.

I did the math quickly. It worked out perfectly. It took three sixteen year olds to equal one forty-seven year old. Roughly three to one. I filed that one away for future reference. I was sure it would come in handy sooner or later.

The point is, the weight I viewed as "light" based on what I had lifted when I was younger was actually an extremely heavy weight. And here I was, close to the half-century mark, performing ten singles with it—and coming back a week later and doing the very same thing!

What happened next was not surprising.

I was doing presses one day, and the bar felt extra heavy, and I twisted a bit to get it up, and I tweaked my lower back.

The next time I trained presses I tweaked my shoulder.

The next time I tried, the bar felt like lead, and I only got four or five singles, missed a few times, and had to call it a day.

And so it went, and the more I tried, the more often I tweaked something—and I was doing the same thing in my other exercises (training too heavy and aggravating all of the aches and pains that accumulate over time), and one day I did deadlifts with a pair of 180 pound steel beams with handles attached to them, and ended up with lower back spasms that lasted for two weeks and twisted me like a pretzel—and I ended up getting so disgusted that I stopped lifting for several years and did nothing but body-weight training.

In retrospect, the problem wasn't the iron.

The problem was me.

I was training too heavy, too often.

I didn't realize that as an older lifter, I needed to do things differently than when I was younger.

As an older lifter, you're going to find that things that worked really well when you were younger don't work nearly as well for you—or don't work at all—or only work in a negative fashion, such as causing debilitating soreness or chronic injuries.

Everyone is different in this regard, but we're all similar—so I'm going to go over some specific points that apply in my own case, and may apply in yours, as well. At the very least, this information should get you thinking about your own program and about things to do to refine your training as you grow older.

## 5 × 5 VARIATIONS

There are several variations of the 5 × 5 system, and they're all effective. But they all have different pros and cons for older lifters. Different variations may work best for you for certain purposes or at different points in your training cycles—and different variations may work better for you at different stages of your career.

The classic 5 × 5 system as used by Reg Park back in the 1950's calls for two progressively heavier warm-up sets followed by three sets of five reps with your working weight. The weight jumps are to be the same from set to set. The first set is approximately 80% of your working weight, the second set is approximately 90% of your working weight, and the third, fourth and fifth sets are performed with 100% of your working weight.

Your goal for the workout is a total of 25 reps. Even if you can perform more than five reps on any one set, don't do it. Stop at five.

If you cannot perform five reps on each of your three working sets, that's okay. Keep at it, and over time you'll get there—and when you do, it's time to add weight to the bar on your working sets—and to add the same amount of weight to the bar on each of your warm-up sets.

Park described this program in his classic manual, *Strength & Bulk Training for Weight Lifters & Body Builders*, which was published in the fifties and in now available again in a modern reprint edition from Bill Hinbern at www.superstrengthbooks.com. It's a great course, and well worth getting.

At page 12 of the course, under the heading, "Developing a Positive Attitude," Park explains the importance of the "stabilizing principle." He notes that by "stabilizing your last 3 sets on the same poundage until you are able to do sets of 5 repetitions with it before you increase the weights used," you ensure continuous progress by following "sound systemized positive training principles." Park then notes, "You will also always be working within your capabilities which sets up confidence and a positive attitude, both are very important to all weight trainers." You will develop confidence and a positive attitude because "you WILL be handling poundages you KNOW you can succeed with and you will approach it with a positive and determined frame of mind and you WILL continue to get stronger."

So that's the classic, Reg Park style 5 × 5 system—one set of five reps at 80% of your five rep weight, one set of five reps at 90% of your five rep weight, and three sets of five reps with 100% of your five rep weight.

The primary benefit of the classic 5 × 5 program is the stabilizing principle—and the real benefit of the stabilizing principle is to keep the lifter from training too heavy!

I often receive letters or emails from trainees who ask, "Why should I wait until I can do three sets of five reps before adding weight to the bar? Why not add weight as soon as I can perform one set of five reps?"

The answer is simple. If you don't wait until you can perform three sets of five reps, you're not using the stabilizing principle. Instead, you're using what Park referred to as "slap dash training principles."

You're also using a heavier weight relative to your one rep max if you add weight when you can perform one set of five reps rather than three sets of five reps.

The result for all but the most disciplined lifter usually goes something like this. You hit a particular weight—let's say 350 pounds in the back squat—and you perform five reps on your first working set, 4 reps on your second working set, and 4 reps on your third working set. Rather than stabilize at 350 pounds until you can perform three sets of five reps, you add five pounds the next time you perform squats, and manage an ugly set of five reps, followed by one set of four reps and one set of three reps.

Since you got five reps on your first set, you use 360 pounds the next time you train. With this weight, you perform a very ugly set of five reps. Each rep is slow and painful, and you cut the depth on the fourth and fifth reps. You also lean a little too far forward and start to bring your knees in on the final two reps.

On the second set, you get three miserable looking reps that are so slow they'd take an hour to walk across the street. Each rep is high, and each rep is performed with a significant forward lean and lots of inner knee rotation.

The third set looks like the second set, only worse.

In your next squat session, you foolishly load the bar to 365 pounds (because you got five reps on your first set the last time), and you do three very slow, very painful, reps, all of them way too high, and all of them performed out of the groove.

You try a fourth rep and get buried. Good thing you're squatting in a power rack with safety bars under you!

You try a second set and get two miserable reps—and decide to skip your third set.

You wake up the next morning, and your lower back feels out of kilter—and so does your left knee.

And you can see where this is going. You've entered the realm of chronic aches and pains—and a major injury is waiting for you right around the corner.

That's what happens when you ignore the stabilizing principle.

But that doesn't mean the traditional 5 × 5 program is going to work for an older lifter. One of the big problems with the classic 5 × 5 program is that you start way too high. I can't imagine starting my squats, deadlifts or any athletic strength exercise by loading the bar up to 80% of my five-rep max. I need several progressively heavier sets to get warmed up, flexible, and mobile before I want to tackle anything that's remotely heavy. For example, if I'm doing Trap Bar deadlifts and my working weight is 400 pounds for five reps, I'm going to start at 135 pounds for five reps and work up in 40 or 50 pound jumps to my five-rep working weight of 400 pounds. In contrast, if I adhered to the classic 5 × 5 program, I'd perform my first warm-up set with 320 pounds, my second with 360 pounds, and then jump to 400 pounds.

In practice, this means that as an older lifter I'm going to perform way more than two warm-up sets. To go back to the previous example of the Trap Bar deadlift, I might do 135 × 5, 185 × 5, 225 × 5, 275 × 5, 325 × 5, and 365 × 5 for my warm-ups.

This leads to another problem. Six progressively heavier warm-up sets are going to add plenty of tonnage to my workout. They're going to eat into my energy reserves and tap into my recovery ability. And even though these are "warm-up" sets, they're going to give my joints a pounding. All of which means that if I finish the day doing three sets of five reps with 400 pounds, I'll probably end up severely over-trained.

So what do I do?

One option is to stop after performing my first working set of five reps. Another option is to perform one working set of five reps, add ten or twenty pounds and perform one set of three reps, and then add another ten or twenty pounds and do a single.

But wait—I can hear you now!

"Wait a minute!" you say. "You're supposed to do three sets of five reps and use the stabilizing principle. What gives?"

Well, what gives is the fact that for many exercises, an older lifter needs more warm-up sets than the classic 5 × 5 program permits. But the warm-up sets can start to become a workout of their own. So you may find it best to do only one working set and stop there.

But here's what you do NOT do. In your next workout you do NOT add weight to the bar because you performed five reps with your working weight. Instead, you STABILIZE by staying at that weight for a total of four sessions. (In other words, if you do Trap Bar deadlifts once a week, you would stay at 400 pounds × 5 reps for four consecutive weeks.)

This is a different way to use the stabilizing principle. Instead of stabilizing by staying at the same weight until you can perform three sets of five reps, you stay at the same weight for four weeks. You don't move up until you can perform five reps with 400 pounds easily and smoothly, with total control on each rep.

The stabilizing principle also works for a lower number of reps. In my front squats, for example, I often perform a series of warm-up sets starting with a very light weight and working up in small jumps, followed by five sets of two reps with my working weight. I do this because my knees, hips, ankles and lower back take a long time to get warmed up, so I need to start light and perform many warm-up sets. But if I use five reps per set, I do too many reps and end up with stiff, sore, aching knees. That even happens with three reps per set. So I perform only two reps per set to keep the volume and the tonnage down.

If I stayed at two reps per set and worked up to my top weight for two reps, I'd end up pretty close to my one rep max. It would probably be something like 95% of my one rep max. That's heavier than I want to train on a regular basis—but I want to have a challenging and stimulating workout. So what do I do?

I challenge my legs and hips by performing five sets of two reps with something like 80% of my one rep max. That gives me a terrific workout without having to pile a super-heavy weight on the bar, and without performing too many reps. And I know it works, because I'm gradually able to add weight to the squat bar, my legs are growing stronger, thicker and more muscular, and my weights in the power snatch and power clean are going up.

You can fit the stabilizing principle into a simple cycling system very easily. You don't even need to use percentages. For example, here's a four-week cycle for a lifter who performs 5 × 2 in the front squat once per week. Let's assume that he can handle 252 pounds for 5 × 2.

### Week One

Front squat
Progressive warm-up sets (2 reps per set)
5 × 2 with 220 pounds

### Week Two

Front squat
Progressive warm-up sets (2 reps per set)
1 × 2 with 220 pounds
5 × 2 with 230 pounds

### Week Three

Front squat
Progressive warm-up sets (2 reps per set)
1 × 2 with 220 pounds
1 × 2 with 230 pounds
5 × 2 with 242 pounds

## WEEK FOUR

Front squat
Progressive warm-up sets (2 reps per set)
1 × 2 with 220 pounds
1 × 2 with 230 pounds
1 × 2 with 242 pounds
5 × 2 with 252 pounds

Another approach would be to alternate heavy and light weeks. This works well for a lifter who wants to extend his training cycle. For example, the same lifter used in the previous example might extend his front squat cycle by doing the following:

## WEEK FIVE

Front squat
Progressive warm-up sets (2 reps per set)
4 × 2 with 220 pounds
1 × 2 with 230 pounds

## WEEK SIX

Front squat
Progressive warm-up sets (2 reps per set)
1 × 2 with 220 pounds
1 × 2 with 230 pounds
5 × 2 with 242 pounds

## WEEK SEVEN

Front squat
Progressive warm-up sets (2 reps per set)
1 × 2 with 220 pounds
5 × 2 with 230 pounds

## Week Eight

Front squat

Progressive warm-up sets (2 reps per set)

1 × 2 with 220 pounds

1 × 2 with 230 pounds

1 × 2 with 242 pounds

5 × 2 with 252 pounds

The bottom line is this. As an older lifter, you don't need to always add weight to the bar in order to progress. You can make great gains by using the stabilizing principle. Stick with a particular weight until you have developed the ability to handle it with perfect control for the required number of reps. The stabilizing principle will keep you positive and optimistic, save wear and tear on your joints, and keep you moving forward for many years.

# 13

## HOW TO WARM UP PROPERLY

We've touched on this topic in previous chapters, but it deserves a chapter of its own. Warming up the right way is critical for an older lifter. Unfortunately, it's something that very few older lifters bother to do—or know how to do. And since there aren't that many older lifters out there, it's hard to learn how to do it. So let me take you through the entire process, step-by-step and move-by-move.

First of all, older lifters need to begin each workout with a general warm-up. The general warm-up should mimic the movements you will perform in that particular training session, and should focus on the joints and muscle groups that you will be stressing. It should include dynamic movements and static stretches. It should begin slow and easy, and build up gradually.

Your general warm-up should cause you to breathe faster and deeper, and get your heart, lungs and circulatory system working, but it should NOT be a cardiovascular drill. Spending five or ten minutes on an exercise bicycle or a step machine does not provide an adequate warm-up for your strength training workout. Your warm-up must be tailored to your specific needs as a strength athlete.

So let's get down to brass tacks. How do you perform a general workout?

There are an infinite number of variations, but to give you a specific example, I'll tell you what I do.

My current training focuses on (1) front squats, (2) power snatches, (3) power cleans or power cleans and either presses, push presses or jerks, (4) presses, push presses or jerks (taking the bar from squat stands), and (5) Trap Bar deadlifts. These are my primary movements, so my warm-ups are designed to get me ready for them. Luckily, they all hit the same major muscle groups and the same joints, so my warm-up is pretty much the same no matter what I do on any given day.

I always begin by turning on the CD player. I always play the same music for long periods of time—right now, it's the *Rocky Balboa* CD—and I time my warm-up to last through the first three tracks on the CD. That's about twelve minutes. Sometimes I do more, but that's the minimum.

Yeah, I know I could use the clock to time it, but I like to focus on my body and not on keeping time when I train. Using the music as a way of keeping track works well for me. And if you're listening to the right kind of music, it helps you get into your workout.

After turning on the CD player, I usually begin by stretching my ankles. This is a simple stretch where I stand at the back of the lifting platform and lean forward against the garage wall. I keep my feet flat. It's a static stretch for the ankles and Achilles tendons. I stretch gently, release, and repeat several times. Each stretch is a little deeper, with a bit greater range of motion. Nothing exaggerated and nothing extreme. I'm not training to join the Cirque de Soleil.

Next, I stand in the center of the platform and perform one-arm shoulder rotations. Five with each arm, using an overhand motion (like throwing a baseball). Then five with each arm using the reverse motion (like a backstroke in swimming). I do these at a slow to medium speed, not fast. My shoulders aren't ready for fast at this point in the drill.

Next, I hold my arms to the front and rotate my right wrist five or ten times in a clockwise motion. I do the same with my left wrist, and then repeat the motion with each hand moving in a counter-clockwise direction.

Then I stretch my wrists. I raise my right arm, bend at the elbow, and pull my hand back against my shoulder (as if I was catching the bar in the clean or performing a front squat). I press down with my left hand to get a good stretch. I repeat this with my left hand, and do the stretch several times with each hand.

After the wrist stretches, I slowly sink into a full squat and hold the bottom position of the squat as a static stretch.

Next, I move to the far wall of the garage and stand with my right hip against the wall. I reach high overhead with my right hand and extend my arm as high as possible overhead, with the arm against the wall. Then I move my fingers as they press against the wall and gently "walk" my arm a little further to the rear. I stop and hold the position, and then repeat the process. This gives the shoulders and upper back a good stretch. After working the right shoulder, I reverse position and work my left shoulder.

After working each shoulder by itself, I step to the corner of the garage, put each hand on one side of the wall, and lean forward. This is another good shoulder stretch. I perform it with my hands about as far apart as if I was performing a power snatch.

My hands are at shoulder height or a bit higher when I begin the movement.

For my next stretch, I turn around and stand with my back to the corner. I reach high overhead and lean back slightly so my arms are extended behind me, with the back of my hands touching the walls of the garage. In this position, I can thoroughly stretch my shoulders and upper back.

After the shoulder stretches, I go back to the platform and stretch my ankles again, and then do more shoulder circles (faster than before, but not full speed), and another full squat stretch, along with some gentle hamstring stretches and side stretches. I also do wrist stretches with my hands pressed against the wall as I lean forward. I do these with my fingers rotated up, to the side and down.

I then move to the center of the lifting platform, lace my fingers together and turn my hands out (keeping my arms straight). This is another good wrist stretch. I follow this by lowering back to a full squat position, and performing the same stretch in the squat position, and then performing the stretch with my arms raised overhead.

At this point, I begin a series of broomstick stretches for my shoulders. I perform overhead presses and wide grip shoulder stretches and dislocates. I do very slow overhead squats. I perform very slow shoulder shrugs and high pulls. I put the broomstick on my shoulders and perform front squats. If I'm going to be doing push presses or jerks, I do those with the broomstick. If I'm going to be doing power cleans or power snatches, I do those with the broomstick. On all of the broomstick exercises, I move slowly. Going out and throwing a broomstick up and down as fast as you can is silly. Doesn't do you any good and could easily hurt something, because even now, you're not warmed-up. You're only halfway there.

146

Let me note here that Jim Schmitz and several other top lifting coaches like their lifters to perform gut work as part of their general warm-up—and Mr. America and Mr. Universe Bill Pearl used to do the same thing. Nothing heavy and nothing dramatic, just some bent legged sit-ups or crunches, leg raises and side bends. I don't do these, but it's something I might try in the future, and it's something you might want to try.

The next step in my warm-up is to perform a few more reps with the broomstick for the first exercise in my workout, followed by reps with an empty barbell. I move a little bit faster on these, but not anywhere near full speed.

Everyone knows that you begin with a light weight when you do your warm-ups and gradually work up to heavier weights, but few people understand that you do the same thing with rep speed. In other words, you begin with slow reps, and gradually increase your rep speed as you perform more sets and your body becomes better lubricated, looser and more mobile. I usually take three or four sets before I'm moving at top speed.

In any case, I begin with the empty bar, and perform one to three sets of three to five reps in whatever movement I will use to start my actual workout. From there, I work up in 22-pound (10 kilo) jumps. There's no magic to the number, it's just that my lightest bumper plates are 5-kilo plates.

To give a concrete example of what I do, let's assume I'm going to begin my workout with power snatches, and my working sets are going to be 132 × 5, 142 × 3, 147 × 1, 154 × 1, 159 × 1, 164 × 1, 169 × 1 and 176 × 1. I might do the following:

General warm-up, 10–20 minutes.

Broomstick power snatch and overhead squat 3–5 sets of 3–5 reps*

Power snatch with empty barbell (44 pounds) 3–5 sets of 3–5 reps**

Power snatch with 5-kilo plates (66 pounds) 3–5 reps**

Power snatch with 10-kilo plates (88 pounds) 3–5 reps**

Power snatch with 15-kilo plates (110 pounds) 3–5 reps***

Power snatch with 20-kilo plates (132 pounds) 3–5 reps (first working set)***

* Slow to medium speed reps

** Medium speed, increasing slightly from set to set.

*** Fast speed.


All in all, my warm-ups would take 20 to 30 minutes from the time I step into the garage until the time I begin my first working set with 132 pounds. That may seem like a lot of time, but for an older lifter with stiff joints, it's necessary. And if the extra warm-up time keeps me healthy, saves my joints, and keeps me lifting longer, then every minute is worth it.

# 14

---

# "BURY ME BIG!"

There's a goofy slogan they put on t-shirts, sweatshirts and ragtops for bodybuilders and powerlifters: "BURY ME BIG!" You can find it right there with the other over-the-top "macho" t-shirts. It's probably almost as big a seller as "Dianabol—Breakfast of Champions" and it's just as infantile.

The problem is, the "Bury me big!" mentality isn't limited to an awkward adolescent dreaming of the day when he'll be bigger than Mr. Olympia and have to hire bodyguards to keep the chicks from mobbing him. The "Bury me big!" mentality is deeply imbedded in the psyche of many older lifters—and it's something they need to drop, and drop fast.

Here's how it all started. The vast majority of older lifters got started when they were teenagers, and most of them were pretty skinny. The big attraction of weight training was the idea of gaining twenty, thirty or even forty pounds of muscle and being bigger than all the other guys.

Knowing full well what was happening, the muscle mags wrote article after article promising big gains in bodyweight in less time than it took the ghostwriter to pen the article!

Bob Hoffman sold "Hoffman's Quick Gain Weight" protein powder in big four pound canisters. It came in two flavors, chocolate and vanilla, and no one has ever been able to decide which tasted worse. If you couldn't stand the "Ick factor," there was Hoffman's Gain Weight Hi-Proteen, which was almost tolerable by comparison, although feeding it to a dog would have amounted to animal cruelty in many states.

For the more scientific and less adventurous, we had Hoffman's Super Gain Weight Tablets, which contained liver, iron and vitamin B-12. The latter had been added shortly after news leaked that President Kennedy was taking regular injections of Vitamin B 12 (just as bodybuilder Steve Reeves had been rumored to do several years earlier). If it was good enough for the President of the United States, it couldn't hurt. Especially if the stories about JFK and Marilyn Monroe were true, and who knew for sure? And if all else failed, you could always try Hoffman's Quick Gain Weight candy bars, which masked the terrible taste of the stuff with peanut butter, chocolate, molasses, coconut and honey.

Meanwhile, Joe Weider pushed can after can of Crash Weight Gain Formula No. 7, which he sold not only through the pages of his various muscle magazines, but through sports magazines, men's magazines and even comic books. Just imagine it. If you were skinny as a rail and the kids called you names like "Toothpick," "Bean-pole," or the really clever one, "Skinny," you couldn't even escape your misery by reading about the amazing adventures of Spiderman. There was Joe Weider, the Trainer of Champions, and there was Dave Draper or Larry Scott or Harold Poole or Chuck Sipes, and there were half a dozen girls busting out of their bikinis and looking at the Muscle God as if they were going to pounce on him at any moment, and there was the singularly well-endowed Betty Weider wearing the world's tiniest leopard-skin bikini, and you just knew she was totally nuts about the

Muscle God—and if you ordered a fourteen-day supply of Crash Weight Gain Formula No. 7, that guy with the muscles would be YOU in record time. And if you turned the page and read the comic book, you'd be "Skinny" for the rest of your life.

For those who couldn't afford the high-priced Gain Weight supplements (and who could, when Crash Weight Gain Formula No. 7 cost a dollar a can—big money back in those days!), there were homemade versions of the infamous "Get Big Drink." They all followed the same pattern. You started with a quart or two of whole milk, and added anything and everything you could find that would up the calories and the protein content: peanut butter, corn syrup, molasses, honey, coconut milk, wheat germ oil, ice cream, flavored yogurt, nonfat dry milk powder, condensed milk, raw eggs, bananas, berries, malted milk powder, Ovaltine, chocolate syrup, soy powder, brewer's yeast, dessicated liver powder, cream, half and half, artificial flavoring, and the protein powder of your choice. You mixed it up in a blender or a big mixing bowl, poured it into a big bottle, put it into the fridge, and chugged two big glasses of the stuff at every meal and in-between every meal.

Meanwhile, article after article in *Strength & Health, Muscular Development* and *IronMan* taught readers how to use the "breathing squat" program combined with the "six meal a day bulking diet" and a gallon a day of the "Get Big Drink" to pack on the pounds. Many readers tried the program, and those who stuck with it typically achieved rapid gains in bodyweight—and amazingly, for many guys, much of the extra weight was solid muscle. Heck, I followed the program back when I was in seventh grade, and grew from 83 pounds to 102 pounds in a little over three months. I was hooked—and so was everyone else.

There was only one problem.

The "get big" program is supposed to be a temporary program to help the scrawny beginner pack on those desperately needed initial pounds. It's not intended as the way to train and eat for the rest of your life. Nor is it intended as the type of program to follow when you're in your forties, fifties or sixties and you're already four times bigger and stronger than the average man.

But the magazines rarely made this clear (after all, they were writing articles for teenagers and young men, not for older lifters), and as a result, many of us are still obsessed with "getting big" long after we've already achieved all the bigness we can handle and need to focus on life-long strength and health.

We'd do better to keep John Grimek's example in mind. Grimek was born in Perth Amboy, New Jersey on June 17, 1910 (or June 18, 1911, according to some accounts). He started weight training as a teenager, using his older brother's Milo Barbell Company weight set (a fact that prompted the inevitable line, "His brother got the weights, and John got the muscles"). Grimek's young body responded to his training program with amazing speed, and by his late teens or early twenties he was remarkably well-developed and ferociously strong.

Grimek soon became interested in competitive Olympic weightlifting, and amazed lifting fans both with his strength (especially in the two hands military press) and with his physique. No one had ever seen anyone like him. In an era when the Heavyweight Boxing Champion of the world might weigh as little as 170 pounds—when the heavyweight wrestling champion might weigh 200 pounds or a bit more—when many pro football running backs weighed 150 to 160 pounds, and many lineman tipped the scales at 200 pounds—when the average man weighed in the 130 to 140 pound range—and when comics and Big Little books featured action adventure heroes who were viewed as the height of massive muscularity while weighing only 160 or 165 pounds— Grimek weighed over 200 pounds of solid, rock-hard muscle, with incredibly thick arms and legs, absurdly huge shoulders and the smallest waist imaginable on a man so large and muscular. This was at a height officially reported as 5′ 8″—which some have suggested was about one inch too generous.

In 1936, Grimek won the heavyweight class at the United States Senior Nationals, setting an American record of 258½ pounds in the Military Press. He was selected to represent the United States in the Olympic Games in Berlin. After the competition, Grimek cut back on his training, did squats and military presses (his two favorite exercises) and not much else, took it easy, lay in the sun, ogled the girls, and chowed down mightily on the good German food (and perhaps the good German beer, as well). His weight shot up to 230 pounds, but his waist remained small and trim—and his proportions were unreal. This was at 26 years of age.

Grimek came back to the States, cut back on his diet, trained a bit more, and continued to compete in Olympic weightlifting competitions. In 1939, he entered and won his first bodybuilding contest. The following year he walked away with the Mr. America title. He repeated the Mr. America victory the following year, prompting an immediate rule change that prohibited former winners from entering the Mr. America contest. Had it not been for the rule change, Grimek probably would have continued to win the championship for at least the next ten or twelve years.

In 1948, at 38 years of age, Grimek won the Mr. Universe title in London, defeating 21-year old Steve Reeves. In 1949, Grimek entered the Mr. USA contest—an event packed with several past winners of the Mr. America contest, and viewed then and now as the toughest contest of the era—and captured first place with a resounding victory, defeating Steve Reeves, Clarence Ross, George Eiferman, Armand Tanny and other highly touted and much younger champions. Grimek retired from bodybuilding competition undefeated. Even today, more than sixty years after his last victory, many rank him as the most perfectly developed man of all time.

Now, here's the critical point. Grimek did his weight gaining as a young man. His last "bulking up" period was in 1936, when he was 26 years old. After that, he cut his weight from a high of 230 pounds to a competition weight variously reported at around 190 to 205 pounds. And after he retired from competition at age 39, he maintained his strength and muscle mass, but never tried to get any bigger. In fact, he was careful not to get bigger, and actually trimmed down (rather than bulking up) for the posing exhibitions he performed in the 1950's. His articles in *Strength & Health* reflect this focus, with many of them covering topics such as weight reduction and controlling the size of your waist and hips through diet and exercise.

As a result, Grimek remained strong, powerful, healthy and fit for the rest of his life—and he continued to look like a champion, with broad shoulders, thick arms and a trim waist even when he was in his sixties and seventies.

Had Grimek continued to train for ever-greater muscle mass—had he continued to try to "Get Big"—had he decided that weighing 230 was fun and weighing 250 might be even more fun—he would have been BIG but he wouldn't have been GREAT.

We can't all be John Grimek. He was the one and only. But we can follow his example. We can train for increased muscle mass when we're young—and later, when we're older, we can decide we're big enough—and we can focus on staying strong, hard and muscular until the end of our days.

I know that mixing and chugging the Get Big Drink was lots of fun—but it's time to move on.

# 15

## CARDIO TRAINING FOR OLDER LIFTERS

"Cardio" is one of the most dreaded words in the English language—or at least it seems that way, judging by the reaction you get whenever you say "cardio" to a dyed-in-the-wool Iron Slinger.

Of course, "heart attack" is another word (two of them actually) that none of us like to hear.

"Fat" is another bad one.

"Over the hill" is another painful one. (Okay, three painful ones.)

So is "old, tired and out of gas." (That's six words, but some of them really hurt.)

If you think about it, it's really strange. We all know that cardio training has tremendous benefit for an older lifter. If you do it right, it helps keep you young. Revs up your circulatory system. Strengthens your heart and lungs. Increases circulation. Helps fight the Lard Lumps. Keeps you lean, hard and muscular. Helps you say hello to your abs again. Increases your energy.

Gives you pep. Puts the "Z" back in your zip. Does good things for your waistline, your pulse rate, your blood pressure and maybe even your cholesterol levels. Keeps your wife interested. Keeps your doctor from nagging you. Gives you something to do on those nights when you're not training and you just know you'll go stark raving mad if you spend just one more minute staring at the talking heads on the Idiot Box.

The problem is, you've tried that cardio stuff and it doesn't work. Not for an older guy with sore knees, sore ankles, sore hips, and a sore lower back. Not for a guy who weighs over 200 pounds. Do you know what happens to your fifty year old knees when you weigh 220 pounds and go out and jog for a mile? And how is that little jogging session going to affect your next squat workout?

No thanks, you say. I'll stick to the weights.

That's fine. But promise me this. Promise me you're going to start to do some cardio training with weights.

It's easy to do, it's fun, it's challenging and there are lots of different ways to do it. Here are some of the best.

## CARDIO SQUATS

We all know that back squats are one of the very best exercises for building strength and muscle mass throughout the entire body. But guess what? They can also build plenty of cardiovascular fitness. And you can do this without making any changes in your regular strength training program.

The next time you do squats, go through your regular routine exactly as scheduled. When you've finished your strength work, drop the bar to a light weight. Try anywhere between 95 and 135 pounds the first time you do this.

Now do five sets of five reps in the regular back squat. Perform each rep at your regular speed, not in a silly jack-rabbit bunny bounce style. Bouncing up and down, even with a light weight, is really hard on your knees, hips and lower back. Even though these are light squats, do them with concentration and purpose, using the same rep speed and the same form you would use with heavier weights.

Rest two minutes (time it) between sets. Walk around and breathe deeply in-between sets.

You'll probably be sore the next day—and you'll be glad you didn't start out with five sets of ten reps, which is where we're going to be going.

After your next squat workout, do five sets of six reps with the same weight you used in your first workout. Again, rest two minutes between sets, and walk around in-between sets. Keep moving the entire time.

The next time you do squats, do 5 sets of seven reps for your cardio work—then five sets of eight reps, and so on until you are doing five sets of ten reps.

At this point, you can do several things. One option is to add reps, so that you gradually work up to 5 sets of fifteen or even twenty reps. That will give your heart and lungs a terrific workout. The problem is, it may lead to overtraining, and it may make you too stiff and too sore—even if you only use 95 to 135 pounds on the bar. So consider trying option two.

Option two is to gradually reduce the rest periods between sets. Time yourself, and gradually reduce your rest time from two minutes to one minute—and then from one minute to thirty seconds. Five sets of ten reps with 95 to 135 pounds in the squat may not get you ready to run a marathon, but it will get you into pretty good shape.

After reducing rest periods, you can try mixing your squats with other exercises, as detailed in the next section.

The 5 × 10 squat program also works well with front squats,

deadlifts, and Trap Bar deadlifts. Don't use it for athletic style movements, such as power cleans or power snatches unless you have very good form and you know that you'll be able to do your reps in perfect form even as you get tired.

## CARDIO SUPERSETS

Once you've mastered the 5 × 10 squat program for cardio training, try doing cardio supersets. Cardio supersets help you increase your cardio training without adding too much extra volume to your workout.

There are several different ways to perform cardio supersets. One of the simplest is as follows.

Let's say you're going to perform the following strength and muscle building workout, and you want to add some cardio training with weights:

1.  Power clean 5 × 3
2.  Military press 5 × 5
3.  Back squat 5 × 5
4.  Barbell bent-over row 3 × 10/8/6
5.  Close grip bench press 3 × 8–10
6.  Barbell curl 3 × 6–8
7.  Crunch 2 × 10–15
8.  Hyperextension 2 × 10–12

If you want to add a super effective cardio component to the workout, try this:

1. Power clean 5 × 3
2. Military press 5 × 5
3. Back squat 5 × 5
4. Barbell bent-over row 3 × 10/8/6
   supersetted with cardio squat—1 × 10 with 135 pounds
5. Close grip bench press 3 × 8–10
   tri-setted with
6. Barbell curl 3 × 6–8
   and cardio squat 1 × 10 with 135 pounds
7. Crunch 2 × 10–15
   supersetted with
8. Hyperextension 2 × 10–12

As you can see, you've turned the entire second part of your program—the part that focused primarily on auxiliary exercises—into a terrific cardio workout by combining some of your exercises with cardio squats and by performing the others in superset style.

Another effective way to restructure the workout for extra cardio benefit would be to do your cardio squats for 5 × 10 after your regular squats. After the cardio squats, work through your remaining exercises, performing them in tri-set and super-set style so that you keep your heart rate elevated for the remainder of the workout. The program would look like this:

1. Power clean 5 × 3
2. Military press 5 × 5
3. Back squat 5 × 5
4. Cardio squat 5 × 10 with 135 pounds, resting 30–60 seconds between sets
5. Barbell bent-over row 3 × 10/8/6 tri-setted with
6. Close grip bench press 3 × 8–10 and
7. Barbell curl 3 × 6–8
8. Crunch 2 × 10–15 supersetted with
9. Hyperextension 2 × 10–12

Another way to perform cardio supersets is to superset barbell and dumbbell exercises with a cardio movement and do this with every exercise in your workout. For your cardio movement, use one of the following—or anything else that you feel like doing:

Bodyweight squats
Pushups
Bent-legged sit-ups
Hanging knees to chest or hanging leg raises
Any other gut exercise(s) you enjoy
Bench step-ups (no weight)
Sledgehammer work (e.g., hitting an old truck or tractor tire or a sand-pit)
Jumping rope
Hitting the heavy bag

Any sandbag exercise for 10–20 reps
Rope climb if it's fairly easy for you
Jog in place
Pull-ups or dips if they're fairly easy for you
Stationary bicycle for 1–3 minutes
Stairmaster for 1–3 minutes
Versa-Climber for 1–3 minutes
Rowing machine for 1–3 minutes
Any other cardio machine you enjoy for 1–3 minutes
Medicine ball drills
A short sprint if you have the room for it and your knees and
    ankles are okay
The farmer's walk
Tire flips
Sled pulling
Any lugging and loading drill that you enjoy

Here's an example of how to put a program together. Let's say your strength training program looks like this:

1. Trap Bar deadlift 5 × 5
2. Incline press 5 × 5
3. Hammer curl with dumbbells 3 × 6–8
4. Close grip bench press 3 × 6–8
5. Hanging knees to chest 2 × 10–12

Your complete program, with cardio supersets, might look something like this this:

1. Trap Bar deadlift 1 × 5
2. Step machine for 2 minutes
3. Trap Bar deadlift 1 × 5
4. Step machine for 2 minutes
5. Trap Bar deadlift 1 × 5
6. Step machine for two minutes
7. Trap Bar deadlift 1 × 5
8. Step machine for two minutes
9. Trap Bar deadlift
10. Step machine for two minutes
11. Incline press 1 × 5
12. Sledge hammer tire smash 10 times per side
13. Incline press 1 × 5
14. Sledge hammer tire smash 10 times per side
15. Incline press 1 × 5
16. Sledge hammer tire smash 10 times per side
17. Incline press 1 × 5
18. Hanging knees to chest 1 × 10–12
19. Incline press 1 × 5
20. Medicine ball throw 10 times
21. Hammer curl with dumbbells 3 × 6–8
    tri-setted with
22. Close grip bench press 3 × 10–12
    and
23. Medicine ball throw 10 times
25. Hanging knee raise 1 × 10–12

Of course, there are endless options for a program utilizing cardio supersets. Once you understand the basic principle, you can put together a variety of productive and effective training programs.

## CONVENTIONAL TRI-SETS AND SUPER SETS

I'm not a fan of conventional bodybuilding. I couldn't even tell you the name of this year's Mr. Olympia winner—or last year's winner—or whether they still conduct the contest. I'm a strength guy, I train for strength, speed, power, and athleticism, and I train in my garage. There's nothing about modern bodybuilding that remotely interests me. BUT—and this is important, so pay attention—I do recognize that some of what bodybuilders do can be of benefit to older lifters.

Many bodybuilders use supersets and tri-sets to train fast, do a high volume workout, and get a big pump.

But there's a different way to use supersets and tri-sets. Older lifters who hate "cardio" can use supersets and tri-sets for cardio training.

Remember, cardio training is all about movement. It doesn't matter whether you're moving your feet up and down on a Stairmaster machine, running laps on a track, jumping rope, hitting the heavy bag, or using a rowing machine. As long as you're moving, you're working your heart, lungs and circulatory system.

You can do the same thing with a workout that keeps you moving. Or you can do it with twenty or thirty minutes of super-set or tri-set training after you complete your heavy stuff. All you do is train your auxiliary movements and gut work in super-set or tri-set fashion, with minimal rest periods in-between your supersets and tri-sets.

Here's an example of what I mean:

1. Power clean 5 × 3, 1 × 2, 1 × 1
2. Press or push press or jerk 3 × 3, 2 × 2, 1 × 1
3. Front squat 5 × 3
3. Incline press 3 × 8–10
   supersetted with
4. Pull-down to chest 3 × 8–10
5. Hammer curl with Log Bar 3 × 6–8
   supersetted with
6. Alternate dumbbell press 3 × 10–12
7. Hanging knees to chest 2 × 12–15
   supersetted with
8. Hyperextension 2 × 12–15

Another option, as discussed earlier, would be to alternate heavy strength workouts with "bodybuilding" workouts where you train lighter, faster, and do super-sets and tri-sets to get a good cardio workout with weights every other time you train. It's not a bad program, and it may actually help your heavy lifting by pumping plenty of blood through your body. Remember, that pump may help you minimize soreness, stiffness and inflammation. Think of it as "active rest"—as something you're dong to enhance your recovery from your heavy strength-oriented workouts.

## PHA TRAINING

PHA training is the brainchild of bodybuilder Bob Gadja, who won the Mr. America, Mr. USA and Mr. Universe titles back in the 1960's. For several years, PHA training was all the rage. *IronMan* magazine carried numerous articles about it, and pretty soon "everyone was doing it." But like most bodybuilding fads, it soon faded away and was replaced by the next Flavor of the Month. The muscle mags always need something new to write about.

PHA stands for "Peripheral Heart Action." The idea is to train your muscles with traditional bodybuilding exercises without exhausting any muscle group or creating a muscle pump. To do this, you divide your exercises into four or five groups of five movements, and perform each group as a single, non-stop circuit, moving from one exercise to the next without pausing. At the end of your five-exercise circuit, you rest briefly, and then repeat the process.

You can do quite a bit of work in a short period of time with the PHA system, which makes it good for conditioning, and you also can handle respectable weights in your different exercises, which makes it good for strength and muscle building. This also makes it good for older lifters who have limited training time due to job, family and other obligations.

The drawbacks to the system are (1) there's no muscle pump, which translates to limited muscle growth for some men, and which doesn't appeal to those who enjoy the feeling of a pump, (2) it's hard to perform a good, multiple set warm-up for lifts such as deadlifts or squats, (3) you can't perform athletic style exercises very well in the context of a PHA program, and (4) you need enough equipment to be able to perform five different exercises. But none of these are significant limitations.

You can't get a pump with the PHA system, so if that's a problem for you, try something else or do PHA one day and conventional training another day. The other issues can be managed. If you want to include power cleans, power snatches or other athletic style exercises in your program, then do them at the start of your workout, and finish things up with some PHA work. As far as problems with warm-ups and equipment, you can work around them with a little bit of creativity.

Here's an example of a three-day per week program that combines athletic strength training and PHA training. The program is designed for a trainee who works out in a home-gym and has relatively limited equipment. Note that the lifter will begin each workout with standard strength training exercises performed for multiple sets of low reps. After the strength training, he'll do a five-exercise PHA circuit five times.

## *Workout A*

1. Power snatch 3 × 5, 3 × 3, and 3 × 1 (add weight on each set)
2. Snatch grip high pull 3 × 3 (use your first 1-rep weight for power snatches)
3. PHA Circuit—Repeat five times:
   a. Press off racks 5 reps
   b. Hanging knees to chest 1 × 10–12
   c. Sledge hammer tire smash—10–12 per side
   d. Pull-up 1 × 5–10
   e. Alternate dumbbell raise 1 × 10–12 per arm

## Workout B

1. Power clean 3 × 5, 3 × 3, and 3 × 1 (add weight on each set)
2. Clean grip high pull 3 × 3 (use your first 1-rep weight for power cleans)
3. Push press or jerk from squat stands 3 × 3, 3 × 2, and 3 × 1 (add weight on each set)
4. PHA Circuit—repeat five times:
   a. Alternate dumbbell curl or dumbbell hammer curl 6–10 reps per arm
   b. Prone hyperextension 1 × 10–15
   c. Sandbag loading exercise with 50-pound sandbag 1 × 10–25
   d. Pushup with feet elevated 1 × 20–30
   e. Pull-up 1 × 5–10 or dumbbell lateral raises 1 × 10–12

## Workout C

1. Front squat 5 × 2 progressively heavier warm-ups, then 5 × 2 working sets
2. PHA Circuit—Repeat five times:
   a. Dumbbell bench press 10–12 reps
   b. Barbell bent-over rowing 10–12 reps
   c. Dumbbell side bend 10–20 reps per side
   d. Front raise with 45 pound plate 1 × 10–15
   e. Bent-legged sit-up 10–12

Another way of doing things would be to alternate strength training workouts with PHA workouts. Here's an example of how you might arrange such a program. Note that you'll perform two strength training workouts and one PHA workout during the first week of your program. During the second week of your program, you'll perform two PHA workouts and one strength training workout. Note that in your PHA workouts, you'll perform three different circuits for a really good cardiovascular, heart and lung workout—and note that each PHA circuit will include one or two exercises designed to keep your heart and lungs working extra hard. In addition, the PHA programs will combine barbell, dumbbell and bodyweight exercises with sandbag exercises, so you'll be doing a variety of different exercises. On the PHA days, remember that the idea is to perform a series of rapid circuits with minimum rest between sets and between circuits. Keep the weights fairly light, whether you're doing an exercise with barbells, dumbbells or sandbags. On bodyweight exercises, work hard but not to complete failure. This is a conditioning workout, not a strength and power workout.

This program is designed for a home gym trainee who prefers to use squats, bench presses, military presses, barbell bent-over rowing and Trap Bar deadlifts for the strength training part of his program:

**Week One**

## Workout A—Strength Training

1. Military press 5 × 5
2. Trap Bar deadlift 5 × 5
3. Barbell bent-over rowing 5 × 5

## *Workout B—PHA Training*

### Circuit No. 1—Repeat 3–5 times

a. Hanging knees to chest 12–15
b. Sandbag lift from floor to shoulder (alternating shoulders on each rep) 10–20
c. Jump rope 1 × 2 mins
d. Pushup with feet elevated 1 × 10–25
c. Alternate dumbbell curl 6–8
e. Two dumbbell squat and press combo 10–15

### Circuit No. 2—Repeat 3–5 times

a. Alternate dumbbell press 6–8
b. One dumbbell side-bend 10–12 reps per side
c. One-arm dumbbell rowing 6–8 per side
d. Sandbag clean and press 10–12
e. Sandbag squat (while holding sandbag in bear-hug) 10–12

### Circuit No. 3—Repeat 3–5 times

a. Medicine ball throw 10–12 times
b. Bent-legged sit-up 12–15
c. Step-up onto bench (no weight) 15–20 per leg
d. Incline dumbbell press or dumbbell bench press 6–8
e. Reverse curl or dumbbell hammer curl 6–8

## Workout C—Strength training

1. Bench press or incline press 5 × 5
2. Back squat or front squat 5 × 5
3. Trap Bar deadlift from blocks or Trap Bar shrug 5 × 5

### Week Two

## Workout A—PHA Training

### Circuit No. 1—Repeat 3–5 times

   a. Sandbag loading drill (lift sandbag from floor to platform 3–4 feet high) 10–20

   b. Pull-up 5–10

   c. Alternate dumbbell raise 10–12

   d. Sledge hammer tire smash 10–12 per side

   e. Side plank 30–60 seconds per side

### Circuit No. 2—Repeat 3–5 times

   a. Jump rope 2 mins

   b. Dumbbell curl and press 6–10

   c. One arm sandbag loading exercise 10–20 per arm

   d. Sandbag squat (sandbag on right shoulder) 10–20

   e. Trap Bar deadlift (light weight only!) 10–12

### Circuit No. 3—Repeat 3–5 times

   a. Alternate dumbbell press 6–8

   b. Plank 30–60 seconds

   c. Sandbag squat (bag on left shoulder) 10–20

   d. Pushup 20–30

   e. Hang from pull-up bar 30–60 seconds

## Workout B—Strength training

   a. Press or bench press 5 × 5

   b. Trap Bar deadlift or bent-over row 5 × 5

   c. Back squat or front squat 5 × 5

## Workout C—PHA Training

**Circuit No. 1—Repeat 3–5 times**

   a. Tire flip or sandbag curl and press 10–12

   b. Step-up onto bench (no weight) 15–25 per leg

   c. Barbell curl 6–8

   d. Close grip bench press 6–8

   e. Sandbag upright row 10–12

**Circuit No. 2—Repeat 3–5 times**

   a. Barbell curl 6–8

   b. Hanging knees to chest 10–15

   c. Clean and press with sandbag 10–15

   d. Lift sandbag from floor to right shoulder 10 times

   e. Lift sandbag from floor to left shoulder 10 times

**Circuit No. 3—Repeat 3–5 times**

   a. Back squat (light!) 10–12

   b. Sandbag bent-over row 12–15

   c. Pull-up 5–10

   d. Pushup with feet on bench 10–25

   e. Bent-legged sit-up 10–12

# 16

---

# MORE CARDIO TRAINING IDEAS

Cardio training is so important for older lifters—and so often neglected by guys who "just want to lift weights"—that I'm going to give you even more ideas about how to combine cardio training and strength training. Pay careful attention to these chapters. Cardio training is important!

The training ideas in this chapter are ways to concentrate on strength training while increasing the conditioning value of your workouts. They'll help you build high levels of strength and conditioning.

## FIVES

If you can perform power snatches, power cleans, and jerks, training them for sets of five reps will give you a terrific workout that will simultaneously build strength, power and cardiovascular fitness. I use this approach in many of my current workouts, and really like it. And let me just say this. If anyone ever says you can't train your heart and lungs with weights, teach them how to do power snatches and have them try some "fives." Or the power clean and press or push press. Then see what they say about training your heart and lungs with weights.

Fives are simply sets of five reps in the power snatch, the power clean, and the clean and press (or the clean and push press or the clean and jerk). You start each rep from the platform. For example, if you were performing power snatches, you'd start the first rep from the platform, lift it overhead, lower the bar back to the platform, get set, and repeat. There's a brief pause between reps as you position the bar and get set for the next rep, so a set of five reps is really a series of five singles with a very short pause between reps.

Roger LaPointe sells a DVD that includes a segment featuring Master's National and World champion Fred Lowe giving a brief demonstration of Olympic weightlifting. At the time, Fred was age 62 and weighed 155 pounds.

After a thorough warm-up, Fred concluded the demonstration by seeing how many consecutive snatches he could perform with the bar loaded to bodyweight. Now, for a Master's weightlifter, performing a single snatch with your own bodyweight is considered to be pretty darn good. At the 2009 United States National Master's weightlifting championships, only three lifters in any weight class in the 60–64 year old division snatched bodyweight or more. In the entire age 55–59 division, only two lifters made bodyweight or higher in the snatch, and in the age 50–54 division, only five lifters managed the feat. So if you're over the age of 50, snatching bodyweight just once is pretty darn good.

But Fred wasn't interested in snatching bodyweight one time.

Heck, he didn't even think three reps was enough.

Or five reps.

Fred powered his way through SEVEN consecutive snatches.

It was pretty darn impressive. And the next time I trained, I made sure to work extra hard on those five-rep sets.

Fives are tough. They challenge your strength, your cardio-vascular fitness and your determination. Give them a try, and see for yourself!

## POWER SUPERSETS

Power supersets are two low-rep strength exercises performed back to back, with no rest between exercises. Unlike bodybuilder supersets, where you use light to medium weights and train for a pump, in power superset training you use heavy weights and do the exercises back to back in order to add some extra conditioning to your strength training program. Different concept, different purpose, different mindset, different exercises and different effect.

At first glance, it would seem impossible to train heavy and do back to back power exercises. But after you get used to it, you'll surprise yourself. If you keep your focus and take things one rep at a time, you'll be able to handle almost as much weight when performing power supersets as you could handle when performing regular sets. This is especially true if you superset a pushing movement with a pulling movement, such as bench press and bent-over rowing.

Examples of power super-sets include the following—all of which are extremely rugged and demanding:

Back or front squat and Trap Bar deadlift
Power snatch and back or front squat
Power clean and back or front squat
Bench press and barbell bent-over row
Incline press and barbell bent-over row
Push press and Trap Bar deadlift
Military press and Trap Bar deadlift
Power clean and Trap Bar deadlift
Power clean and press and Trap Bar deadlift
Back or front squat and power clean
Back or front squat and power clean and press
Power clean and clean grip high pull
Power snatch and snatch grip high pull

An interesting variation of power supersets is to pair full range movements with partial movements. Some examples are:

Military press or push press and Trap bar deadlift from the knees
Power clean and press and Trap Bar deadlift from the knees
Back or front squat and Trap Bar deadlift from the knees
Power clean and Trap Bar deadlift from the knees
Power clean and power clean from blocks
Power snatch and power snatch from blocks
Power clean and clean grip high pull from blocks
Power snatch and power snatch from blocks

Another option is to combine barbell movements with dumb-bell movements or heavy awkward objects. For example, you might try any of the following:

Trap bar deadlift and dumbbell incline press
Back or front squat and alternate dumbbell press
Alternate dumbbell press and barbell bent-over rowing
Sandbag lift from floor to shoulder and Trap Bar deadlift
Back or front squat and sandbag loading exercise
Back or front squat and tire flip
Trap Bar deadlift and tire flip
Trap Bar deadlift from blocks and tire flip
Trap Bar deadlift and two dumbbell curl and press
Back or front squat and sled drag
Back or front squat and car or truck push
Trap Bar deadlift and car or truck push

When performing power super-sets, perform each rep in perfect form. Don't start rushing things. It's not the same as supersetting concentration curls and triceps kickbacks. You're using exercise combinations where you have significant weight on the bar, and you need to give each movement the attention it deserves.

## COMPLEXES

Olympic lifters use complexes to perfect their lifting technique and to build explosive power. They're also very good for con-ditioning. Complexes are similar to power supersets, but you perform two or three movements without letting go of the bar. The power clean and press is one of the best-known and most frequently used complexes. Another well-known example is a power clean from the platform followed by a power clean from the hang—or a power clean from the hang followed by a power clean from the platform. Or two power cleans from the hang followed by one power clean from the platform—or two power cleans from the hang followed by one power clean from the platform and one press (or push press or jerk).

Other examples taken from the arsenal of Olympic weightlifters include:

Power clean and push press

Power clean and jerk

Dead hang power snatch and power snatch from platform

Power snatch from platform and dead hang power snatch

Power clean and clean grip high pull

Power snatch and snatch grip high pull

Clean grip high pull and power clean

Snatch grip high pull and power snatch

Three position power clean

Three position power snatch

Power snatch and overhead squat

Power clean and front squat

Front squat and press, push press or jerk

Power clean, front squat and press, push press or jerk

Dead hang power clean, power clean from platform, and press, push press or jerk

Complexes are usually performed for low reps, because a weightlifter needs to hit each of the different movements with maximum speed and explosiveness and in perfect form. If you try to perform too many reps, your form is likely to break down, so you need to be careful.

One of the most effective complexes for all-around conditioning is the power clean, front squat and press (or push press or jerk) combination. There are several ways to perform this. You can do a power clean, followed by a front squat, followed by a press, push press or jerk, lower the bar to the platform, and repeat for three to five reps. Alternatively you can perform five consecutive power cleans, followed by five consecutive front squats, followed by five consecutive presses, push presses or jerks. Whichever way you do it, you'll get a terrific workout.

By their very nature, Olympic lifting movements lend themselves well to various complexes. Other training methods do not. There's no way to perform an effective complex with the bench press, the back squat or the deadlift. Some men have tried barbell bent-over rowing followed by deadlifts, but the weight is too heavy for rowing and too light for deadlifts. Bob Hoffman's favorite exercise was the squat and press behind neck, but many older lifters have shoulder problems and should stay away from the press behind neck—and besides, the weight is always going to be too heavy for the press behind neck and too light for the squat. However, benches, back squats and deadlifts can be trained very effectively with power supersets, as described in the previous section.

The two-dumbbell curl and press is a good combination exercise. Five or ten reps with each arm will give you a heck of a workout. You can perform the exercise in alternate arm fashion or lifting each dumbbell simultaneously. If your pressing strength surpasses your curling strength, do one curl and two presses on each combination "rep"—or start the set with five or more presses to tire your pressing muscles, and then do one curl followed by one press on each combination "rep."

## BREATHING SQUATS

The 20 rep breathing squat is the core movement in the time-honored weight gaining program developed by Mark Berry way back in the 1930's. The program was used with great success by men like Joseph C. Hise and William Boone, and it helped usher in an era of truly massive muscular development. Prior to the squatting era, there were very few legitimate heavyweight lifters. In short order, we had men like John Grimek, John Davis, and Louis Abele, who used heavy, high rep squatting programs to build enormous muscle mass and develop phenomenal strength and power.

A man named Peary Rader read about the breathing squat program and decided to give it a try. Peary had trained on various exercise programs for over ten years, without gaining an ounce of muscle. He stood around 6' tall and weighed about120 pounds. There's a photo of Peary taken at this point in his career, and his knees were literally bigger than his thighs. But that was soon to change.

Peary embarked on the breathing squat program and over the next two years he gained close to 100 pounds of muscle. Peary was so impressed with his results that he decided to share the breathing squat program with the world. He did so through the pages of *Iron Man* magazine, which he founded, edited and published for the next fifty years. And during that period, tens of thousands of readers used the breathing squat program to pack on pound after pound of muscle. It was one of the most effective muscle-building programs of all time.

In later years, Peary noted that in addition to helping him gain weight, the breathing squat program had given him remarkable cardiovascular fitness. Even when he weighed well over 200 pounds, he had a very low resting pulse rate, and endless stamina. On a vacation in the Colorado Rockies, he was able to run up and down rugged mountain trails all day long, while others labored far behind in the distance, plodding slowly up the steep slopes and struggling for breath in the rarefied mountain air.

Peary put two and two together, and offered the suggestion that lifters use the breathing squat program not merely as way of gaining muscular bodyweight, but as a way of improving cardiovascular condition through weight training.

It's a good idea, and well worth considering. As an older lifter, your primary goal isn't gaining weight (unless you're a beginner and extremely scrawny, or you've lost weight as the result of illness or injury), but you can still benefit enormously from the breathing squat program. All you do is use the breathing squat program without the six meal a day super weight gaining diet that the bulk seekers follow.

An old friend and long-time Iron Slinger, Mike Rinaldi (a good friend, good lifter and good man who unfortunately passed away on June 22, 2008), once suggested the very same thing in an email message to me. "Great program, lousy diet," he wrote. And for an older lifter, that pretty well sums it up.

The classic breathing squat program involves one set of twenty reps in the squat with all the weight you can handle. (As discussed below, older lifters may do better by using no more than bodyweight on the bar.) You take one huge, deep, lung-stretching breath after the first rep—two after the second rep—three after the third rep—four after the fourth rep—and five after each ensuing rep.

When you hit the final rep, you stagger over to your flat bench, collapse on it, and perform one set of twenty breathing pullovers with a pair of very light dumbbells or an empty bar. The pullovers are solely for rib-cage expansion, so you use a very light weight. An empty bar is plenty (and I'm talking about an exercise bar, not an Olympic bar). Or use two very light dumbbells—no more than 20 pounds, no matter how strong you are.

You supplement the squats with a couple of upper body movements. Joe Hise used presses and curls. Peary Rader suggested that trainees perform several sets of bench presses and several sets of barbell bent-over rowing. For those with greater energy reserves, he advised using one set of breathing squats and breathing pullovers supplemented by barbell presses, barbell curls, bench presses and barbell bent-over rowing. Bench presses and pull-downs would be another option, and some have included a set of stiff legged deadlifts to finish the program.

You can perform your other exercises either before or after your squats. If you perform them afterwards, you'll need to rest for ten or fifteen minutes before tackling any additional work. That's how tired the squats will make you.

If you perform the full six-exercise program, you can begin with barbell curls, followed by barbell presses, and then do your squats and pullovers. Take a ten or fifteen minute break, and then finish up with bench presses and bent-over rowing.

Now, before we go any further, let me offer some advice and caution for older lifters. This is important, so please pay careful attention before you run out to the garage, load up the squat bar and try one of those twenty-rep sets.

First and foremost, as an older lifter, you need to be sure your heart and circulatory system is ready for a 20-rep breathing squat program. In other words, get it cleared with your doctor before giving it a try.

Second, the 20-rep squat program may be too hard on your knees, hips and lower back. Remember what I said earlier about low reps for older lifters.

Third, the program may be too hard on your shoulders. They'll get awfully stiff and sore from the weight of the bar, and if you have any existing shoulder problems, the twenty-rep journey probably is not a good idea.

Fourth, you may burn out very quickly from heavy, high rep squats. Remember, you're not a kid any more—and the program that worked great when you were seventeen may not work very well now that you're forty-seven—or fifty-seven—or sixty-seven.

Fifth, no matter who you are or how old you are, you need to break into a high rep squatting program very slowly and carefully. One of the worst pieces of well-intentioned advice in the history of the Iron Game is the oft-repeated dictum to begin your breathing squat program by taking a weight you can handle for ten reps and then forcing yourself to grind out an additional ten reps to make twenty. That's crazy. And for older lifters, it's insane crazy.

The sensible way to start a breathing squat program is to take 50% of your ten-rep weight and perform twenty reps with it. In other words, you want the first workout to be fairly easy. Work up gradually from there. Rome wasn't built in a day, and neither are strongmen—and if you're an older lifter, you ought to have learned the virtues of patience by now. It's both foolish and fool-hardy to jump into a twenty-rep squatting program with heavy weights and end up so sore and tired you can't move for a couple of days. Start light and work up slowly.

By the way—Peary Rader started his breathing squat program with an empty bar. Two years later he was handling 350 pounds. That's an example of how to do things the right way. If Peary had started out with 100 pounds, he might have lasted for only a workout or two.

Sixth, older lifters almost always need several progressively heavier warm-up sets before they begin anything approaching a heavy weight. They also need to get their heart, lungs and circulatory system warmed up. So don't go out and load the bar to a heavy weight, do a few stretches and jump into a heavy set of twenty reps. That might be okay for a younger guy, but it's not going to work for an older lifter.

Finally, you may want to consider the Roger Eells variation of the breathing squat program. Roger Eells was a next-door neighbor, friend and training partner of Iron Game author, Harry Paschall. He operated a gym in Columbus, Ohio, and taught a variation of the breathing squat where you never used more than your own bodyweight on the bar. Bradley J. Steiner also preferred this method of performing twenty-reppers. For older lifters, the limited weight version of the breathing squat program may be a much better approach than the traditional, "use all the weight you can handle" version. Twenty reps with a moderate weight will give anyone a very good conditioning workout.

## TWENTY-REP DEADLIFTS

The twenty-rep deadlift is an alternative to the twenty-rep breathing squat. It's a very good program for older lifters who cannot do squats because of knee, lower back or shoulder problems. If you want to give twenty-rep deadlifts a try, start light and work up gradually—and be sure to perform all of your reps in perfect form! Use the bent-legged deadlift, not the stiff-legged version, and if at all possible, use a Trap Bar.

You can hold onto the bar for the entire set, or you can set it down in-between reps and start each rep from the platform. That's the way I like to perform them. It allows me to get into exactly the right starting position for each rep.

Again, let me emphasize that the twenty-rep deadlift may be too much for an older lifter. The same cautions mentioned in the previous section in connection with the twenty-rep squat are fully applicable to the twenty-rep deadlift.

I should also note that it would NOT be a good idea to try twenty-rep sets on athletic style exercises, such as the power clean or the power snatch. These exercises require perfect technique and split-second timing, and if you perform too many reps your technique gets ragged and you invite an injury.

As with the twenty-rep squat, the twenty-rep deadlift can be performed very effectively with no more than bodyweight on the bar. For older lifters, that's probably the best way to perform the program.

## LUGGING AND LOADING

This one is also known as "carrying stuff." This program was featured by Dr. Ken Leistner in the October, 1994 issue of *Milo*, and like any of Dr. Ken's programs, it's a good one. It has a much different "feel" than conventional cardio, and those of you who can't stand the idea of sitting on an exercise bike or using a step machine for half an hour will find this to be a welcome alternative. It's sort of like moving around while doing weight training exercises—which makes it perfect for dyed-in-the-wool Iron Slingers who are never happy unless they're lifting, holding and carrying stuff. Plus, it's a perfect program for those of you who train at home.

The only "equipment" you need for the "lugging and loading" program is a big pile of "heavy stuff" in one corner of the yard or in a corner of your garage. The heavy stuff can be pretty much anything you like: pieces of scrap metal, old dumbbells, old plates, sandbags, barrels, rocks, cinder blocks, bricks, a bucket or two of water, whatever. It really doesn't matter. Scrounge the stuff from junkyards or just go to a local used sporting good store and buy some cheap plates and dumbbells. If they only have small plates, throw them into a bag or box or tie them together with rope or chain until they're the right weight for you.

To perform the workout, you just carry the stuff piece by piece across the yard and pile it up in the new location. Then you move it back to where it was when you started. Repeat as many times as you want.

You can increase the intensity of the workout by going faster or by carrying heavier stuff. But don't overdo things and turn it into a mini-version of a strongman competition. The idea is NOT to lift something super heavy and stagger back and forth with it. The idea is to carry stuff back and forth for a continuous twenty to forty-five minute cardio workout.

You also can add some bodyweight exercises, light squats or deadlifts, gut work, rope jumping, medicine ball drills, heavier loading drills, tire flips, sledge-hammer training, or anything else you feel like doing. For example:

Carry two dumbbells from the pile of stuff to the other side of the yard.
Do a set of pushups.
Walk back to the garage and perform a set of light squats for 10–15 reps.

186

Walk back to your pile of stuff and grab a rock, carry it across the yard, and set it down in the new pile.

Pick up the two dumbbells and do a set of curl and press.

Walk back to the garage and do a set of light deadlifts.

Jump rope for two minutes.

Walk back to the pile of stuff, grab anything, and carry it over to the new pile.

Do a second set of pushups.

Walk back to the garage and do a set of pull-ups.

Jump rope for two minutes.

Walk back to the pile of stuff, grab something and carry it over to the new pile.

Repeat for twenty to forty-five minutes. If you're having fun, keep going for an entire hour.

The lugging and loading cardio workout is a really good way for an older lifter to get a cardio workout. It's relatively easy on your bones and joints, and it spreads the workload over your entire body. That makes it safer and more effective for sustained training than many other cardio activities. Just be sure to wear sturdy shoes so you won't slip, and wear gloves if you're handling anything that's sharp or rusty. Steel-toed work shoes or work boots might be a good idea depending on what you have in your pile of stuff.

## CONVENTIONAL CARDIO TRAINING

If you're already doing conventional cardio, or if you want to give it a try, you'll need to decide how to combine cardio training and strength training without compromising your recovery ability, interfering with your strength training and causing or aggravating any bone or joint problems. This can be a tough balancing act, especially for trainees who weigh over 200 pounds. The heavier you are, the more limited you are in your cardio training options. For example, a fifty-year old, 250-pound lifter is not a good candidate for a jogging program. The repetitive pounding at 250 pounds is going to be way too hard on his feet, ankles, knees, hips and lower back.

But remember—there are important health benefits from cardio training. And the problems associated with cardio training can be minimized by careful planning.

First, you need to decide if you're going to do your cardio work on the same day you do your strength training. The benefit to doing this is that you then have a complete day of rest before your next workout. For example, if you train Mon/Wed/Fri and combine 45 to 60 minutes of strength training with 20 minutes of cardio work, you get a complete rest on your off days. For some readers, this will be the ideal program.

Other readers will find that a combined strength training session and cardio session is just too tiring for them. These trainees may do better by splitting their strength training and their cardio training into separate sessions. A very common way of doing this is to perform three strength training sessions and three cardio training sessions, so you end up exercising six days per week. For many readers, however, this would be too tiring a program. If you decide to give it a try, use short, abbreviated workouts and some sort of heavy/light/medium approach to both your strength training and your cardio work. If you try to do three long and hard strength training sessions and three long and hard cardio sessions, you're going to end up very sore and very tired—and it's going to happen very quickly.

A better approach for the majority of older lifters would be to do two days of strength training and two days of cardio work.

That gives you a total of four training days and three rest days each week, which will be much easier for most of you to handle. Of course, if you're retired, and really enjoy training more often, go for it—just keep your enthusiasm under control, use abbreviated training and cycle your training intensity.

Another alternative would be a total of three training days each week, alternating between strength training sessions and cardio sessions. This way, you'd perform two strength training workouts and one cardio session in week one, and the reverse in week two. I know this doesn't sound like much, but as an older lifter, you don't NEED very much training. A small amount of quality training goes a long way for an older lifter—and this includes both strength training and cardio work.

However you choose to arrange your weekly program, be sure to protect your joints from back-to-back workouts. For example, don't do a heavy squat workout on Monday followed by a cardio session on Tuesday where you do cycling, stationary cycling, a step machine or anything else that imposes direct stress on your knee joints. It would be much better to follow the squat session on Monday with cardio work on a rowing machine, heavy bag work, or swimming on Tuesday. This would give your knees much more of a rest on Tuesday, and that might make all the difference between healthy joints and having knee replacement surgery at an early age. The same points apply to all other exercises.

As weightlifters, we are conditioned from an early age to think that weight training is "heavy" work, and that cardio training is "light" work. This is why we think we can combine our weight training workouts with cardio sessions on our "off" days. But it doesn't work like that in real life—especially for older lifters. What actually happens is that our cardio sessions end up imposing plenty of wear and tear on our bodies. They may be "light" but they're certainly not stress-free! And that means that we need to plan carefully when we combine them with our weight training sessions.

Here's a related point. It's a very good idea for older lifters to use several different kinds of cardio training. This helps avoid excessive wear and tear on your body. If you do nothing but use an exercise bicycle for your cardio, you're probably going to end up with sore knees. It would be better to mix things up: stationary bicycle one day, step machine another day, and a rowing machine on the next day. Your heart and lungs will thank you for training them—and your joints will thank you for doing the training intelligently.

## STAYING ACTIVE

I'll close this chapter by making a simple suggestion: as you grow older, stay active. Start walking more. Do more yard work. Start a garden. Gardening is great exercise—you dig, you shovel, you lift, you carry, you pull, you drag, you build stuff, and at the end of it all, you get great home-grown vegetables as a reward for all of your hard work.

My wife and I try to have non-car weekends. Meaning that we try to walk everywhere we need to go. It's not too hard. We spend lots of time working in the garden. As far as training goes, I train in the garage, and Trudi trains at home and at a gym located close to the house. The post office is about half a mile away, so if we need to fill book orders, we walk there. There are some coffee shops, restaurants, a bookstore, a movie theatre, a bank and a pharmacy located within easy walking distance. The grocery store is about a quarter of a mile away, and there's a health food store not much further, so if we need supplies, we walk over to the store and carry them back. It's more fun than driving, and although it's not the same as hard cardio or a heavy set of squats, it keeps us active. Plus, we get to spend some time together, take it slow and enjoy life a little.

You may or may not be able to rely 100% on your feet to get around on weekends. Maybe you can do it more often—or perhaps not often at all. It depends on where you live and what resources are available to you. The point is, don't just rely on your workouts to stay in shape. Make it an all day activity. Remember, exercise doesn't have to be "balls to the wall" to pay big dividends in health and fitness.

# 17

## TEN TRAINING PROGRAMS FOR OLDER LIFTERS WHO USE ATHLETIC STYLE EXERCISES

Let's put it all together and outline some effective training programs for older lifters. I know that different readers will have different training goals, different types of equipment, and prefer different exercises and training styles, so I'll offer a variety of different programs. The one constant will be that the programs are designed for home gym training. Of course, those of you who train in commercial gyms will be able to follow the same programs.

Programs 1–10 are for those of you who prefer to train with athletic style exercises, such as power snatches, power cleans, and jerks. This is how I prefer to train, so these workouts are similar to my current training programs. I'll cover these programs in this chapter, and other programs in subsequent chapters. But remember, athletic strength training exercises can be dangerous if you don't know how to perform them properly. They should only be used by readers who know how to perform the exercises—as in, those of you who have been doing power cleans and power snatches for pretty much your entire training career—or those who are competing in Master's weightlifting competition. If you don't know how to perform athletic style exercises, you should follow one of the other types of programs!

Programs 11–20 are for those of you who prefer to use squats, deadlifts and standing presses or bench presses as your primary exercises. The programs feature abbreviated training schedules and divided workouts. These are really good programs for cellar-dwellers and garage gorillas. I'll outline these programs in chapter 18.

Programs 21–30 will be total-body workouts for trainees who are trying to build or maintain a good balance of strength, muscular development and stamina. These programs are based on the teaching of men like Harry Paschall and Bradley J. Steiner, and have proven themselves to be very effective for all-around physical development. These programs will appear in chapter 19.

Programs 31–40 will be PHA and circuit training programs for maximum conditioning benefit. Consider them "cardio training with weights." I'll cover these programs in chapter 20.

Programs 41–50 will feature what I refer to as "ultra-abbreviated training programs." Ultra-abbreviated programs are extremely low in volume, and are designed for trainees with low energy reserves and those who have a great deal of trouble recovering from their workouts. These programs are excellent for older lifters. I'll cover these programs in chapter 21.

As you review the programs, you'll note that there's nothing fancy, nothing exotic and nothing high tech about them. You'll also note that all of the workouts are pretty short. In fact, you may wonder if the printer made a mistake and forgot to print some of the exercises!

But remember, short, abbreviated workouts are exactly what older workers need in order to recover from their workouts and avoid excessive soreness and stiffness. Leave the longer workouts to the younger guys—they're too young to know better!

All of the workouts in this chapter (and indeed, all of the workouts in this book) work very well with a simple cycling system. A four-week training cycle based on 70%–80%–90% and 95–100% works very well for older lifters. At the end of the cycle you can repeat your entire program, or you can begin a new program.

If a workout takes too long to complete, feel free to divide it up or eliminate an exercise here or there. If you feel tired, or your joints are unusually sore or stiff, add an additional rest day or two.

All of the programs in this chapter have fairly low volume, which is important for older lifters. However, programs 9 and 10 have *extremely* low volume. These programs may work better for lifters age 55 and older.

# PROGRAM NO. 1

Program No. 1 is a three-day per week program focusing on athletic strength training. You'll train each exercise once per week.

Note that you begin your training week with power snatches. This is your fastest exercise, and it's best to do it at the start of the week, when you're well recovered. You'll do power cleans and an overhead movement in the second session, and hit squats or front squats during your third workout.

For best results, cycle the program over a period of four weeks: Week One—70%, Week Two—80%, Week Three—90%, Week Four—95–100%.

**Mon**

1. General warm-up 10–15 mins
2. Power snatch 4–5 × 3 (progressively heavier warm-ups), then 3 × 2 (working sets)
3. Snatch grip high pull 3 × 2 (use your top weight for two reps in the power snatch)
4. Plank and side plank (1–2 sets of planks and 1 set of side planks to each side)

**Wed**

1. General warm-up 10–15 mins
2. Power clean and press, push press or jerk 4–5 × 2 (progressively heavier warm-ups), then 3 × 2 (working sets)
3. Clean grip high pull 3 × 2 (use your top weight for two reps in the power clean)
4. Bent-legged sit-up 2–3 × 8–12

**Fri**

1. General warm-up 10–15 mins
2. Back squat or front squat 5–7 × 2–3 (start light and add weight one each set)
3. Hyperextension 2–3 × 10–12
4. Hanging knees to chest 2–3 × 10–12

## PROGRAM NO. 2

Program No. 2 is another three day per week program. The volume is a bit greater in this program, and you'll train some movements twice a week.

As with Program No. 1, a 70%–80%–90%–95–100% cycling system would work very well with this schedule.

**Mon**

1   General warm-up 10–15 mins
2.  Power snatch 3 × 5 (progressively heavier warm-ups), then 3–5 × 2–3 (add weight on each set)
3.  Push press 5 × 3 (progressively heavier sets)
4.  Back squat 5 × 3 (progressively heavier sets)
5.  Bent-legged sit-up 2–3 × 8–12

**Wed**

1.  General warm-up 10–15 mins
2.  Power clean 3 × 5 (progressively heavier warm-ups), then 3–5 × 2–3 (add weight on each set)
3.  Jerk press 5 × 2 (progressively heavier sets)
4.  Front squat 5 × 3 (progressively heavier sets)
5.  Hanging knees to chest 2–3 × 10–15

**Fri**

1.  General warm-up 10–15 mins
2.  Power snatch 3 × 3 (progressively heavier warm-ups), then 3–5 × 2 (add weight on each set)
3.  Power clean 3 × 2 (progressively heavier warm-ups), then 3–5 × 2 (add weight on each set)
4.  Back squat, front squat or Trap Bar deadlift 5 × 3 (progressively heavier sets)
5.  Bent-legged sit–up 2–3 × 8–12

# PROGRAM NO. 3

This is a four-day per week program using athletic strength training exercises. That sounds like a lot of training, but the volume is very low in each workout. In addition, two of the four workouts will be one-exercise sessions, and one will be a light workout. This is a good program for those of you who like to train four days per week and who enjoy short, fast workouts.

If the program is too demanding as a four day per week schedule, train every other day or three days per week and take a few extra days to get through the entire four-day program. For instance, you might take nine or ten days to complete the four workouts.

**Mon**

1. General warm-up 10–15 mins
2. Hang power snatch (2 reps) and power snatch from the platform (1 rep) 5 × 3 (progressively heavier sets)
3. Push press from racks 5 × 3 (progressively heavier sets)

**Tues**

1. General warm-up 10–15 mins
2. Back squat or front squat 5–7 × 2 (progressively heavier sets)
3. Bent-legged sit-ups 2–3 × 8–12

**Thurs**

1. General warm-up 10–15 mins
2. Hang power clean (2 reps) and power clean from the platform (1 rep) 5 × 3 (progressively heavier sets)
3. Jerk from racks 5 × 1 (progressively heavier sets)
4. Military press or incline press 5 × 3 (progressively heavier sets)

**Fri**

1. General warm-up 10–15 mins
2. Back squat or front squat 5–7 × 2 (go light to medium on these)
3. Plank (1 set), and side plank (1 set per side)

## PROGRAM NO. 4

Here's another four-day per week program. This one extends for a two-week period, with a total of eight different workouts. You'll do two heavy workouts and two medium workouts in week one. In week two, you'll do two light workouts, one medium session and one heavy session.

On each exercise, you'll start light and perform a series of progressively heavier sets, finishing with your top weight for the day.

### WEEK ONE

**Mon (Heavy)**

1. General warm-up 10–15 mins
2. Front squat 5 × 3
3. Power snatch 3 × 3, 3 × 2
4. Push press 5 × 2
5. Bent-legged sit-up 2 × 8–10

**Tues (Medium)**

1. General warm-up 10–15 mins
2. Snatch grip high pull 5 × 3
3. Prone hyperextension 2–3 × 10–12

**Thurs (Heavy)**

1. General warm-up 10–15 mins
2. Power clean 3 × 3, 3 × 2
3. Jerk 3 × 2, 3 × 1
4. Back squat 5 × 3

**Fri (Medium)**

1. General warm-up 10–15 mins
2. Clean grip high pull 5 × 3
3. Hanging knees to chest 2–3 × 10–15

## Week Two

**Mon (Medium)**

1. General warm-up 10–15 mins
2. Power snatch 5 × 3
3. Snatch grip high pull 3 × 3 (use your final weight for power snatches)
4. Bent-legged sit-up 2 × 8–12

**Tues (Light)**

1. General warm-up 10–15 mins
2. Front squat 5 × 5 or 5 × 3

**Thurs (Heavy)**

1. General warm-up 10–15 mins
2. Power clean and press, push press or jerk 3 × 3, 3 × 2, 2 × 1
3. Back squat 5 × 3
4. Hanging knees to chest 2 × 10–15

**Fri (Light)**

1. General warm-up 10–15 mins
2. Clean grip high pull 5 × 3

# PROGRAM NO. 5

Program No. 5 is another four-day a week program, but it's a bit different than the other schedules. It incorporates a combination of athletic strength movements and other basic strength training exercises. It's a great program for cellar-dwellers and garage gorillas.

The program covers two full weeks. Week One has two heavy days, one medium day and one light day. Week two has two medium days, one light day and one heavy day.

On each exercise, start light and perform a series of progressively heavier sets, working up to your top weight for the day.

## Week One

**Mon (Heavy)**

1. General warm-up 10–15 mins
2. Power snatch 5 × 3 or 5 × 2
3. Snatch grip high pull 3 × 3
4. Push press 5 × 2

**Tues (Light)**

1. General warm-up 10–15 mins
2. Back squat 5 × 3
3. Bent-legged sit-up 2–3 × 8–12

**Thurs (Heavy)**

1. General warm-up 10–15 mins
2. Power clean 5 × 3 or 5 × 2
3. Jerk 5 × 2
4. Hanging knees to chest 2 × 10–15

**Fri (Medium)**

1. General warm-up 10–15 mins
2. Front squat 5 × 3

## WEEK TWO

**Mon (Medium)**

1. Front squat 5 × 3
2. Power snatch 5 × 2
3. Snatch grip high pull 3 × 2

**Tues (Light)**

1. Trap Bar deadlift 5 × 5 or 5 × 3
2. Bench press or incline press 5 × 5 or 5 × 3
3. Bent-legged sit-up 2–3 × 8–12

**Thurs (Heavy)**

1. Power snatch 5 × 2
2. Power clean 5 × 2

**Fri (Light)**

1. Military press 5 × 5
2. Back squat 5 × 5
3. Hanging knees to chest 2 × 10–15

## PROGRAM NO. 6

Program No. 6 is a two-day per week program. This would work very well with a basic 70%, 80%, 90%, 95–100% cycling schedule.

On each exercise, start light and perform a series of progressively heavier sets, finishing with one set with your top weight for the day.

**Mon**

1. General warm-up 10–15 mins
2. Power snatch 5 × 3 or 5 × 2
3. Snatch grip high pull 3 × 2
4. Push press 5 × 2
5. Front squat 5 × 2
6. Bent-legged sit-up 2 × 8–12

**Thurs**

1. General warm-up
2. Power clean 5 × 3 or 5 × 2
3. Clean grip high pull 3 × 2
4. Jerk 3 × 2, 2 × 1
5. Back squat 3 × 3, 3 × 2
6. Plank (1–2 sets), and side plank (1 set per side)

# PROGRAM NO. 7

Here's another two-day per week program. This one covers two full weeks of training, so you have a total of four different workouts. This will allow plenty of time for maximum recovery between workouts.

This program will focus on athletic strength exercises. It also will include some basic strength and muscle-building exercises to supplement your athletic strength training exercises. You'll build (or maintain) plenty of strength, speed and power on this program—and that makes it ideal for older lifters.

The first week will include one heavy session and one medium session. The second week will include one light session and one medium session.

If you prefer to use a simple cycling program rather than a schedule of light, medium and heavy days, that's fine. You can use the 70%–80%–90%–95–100% cycle described previously. You also could use an eight-week cycle as follows: week one— 70%, week two—80%, week three—85%, week four—90%, week five—70%, week six—80%, week seven—90%, week eight—100%. If you use the cycling schedule, disregard the references to heavy, medium and light days, and use the appropriate percentages for each week of training.

On each exercise, start light and add weight for a series of progressively heavier sets, finishing with your top weight for the day.

## WEEK ONE

### Mon (Heavy)

1. General warm-up 10–15 mins
2. Back squat 5 × 3
3. Power snatch 5 × 2
4. Power clean 5 × 2
5. Push press 5 × 2
6. Plank (1–2 sets), and side plank (1 set per side)

### Thurs (Medium)

1. General warm-up 10–15 mins
2. Front squat 5 × 2
3. Snatch grip high pull 5 × 2
4. Clean grip high pull 5 × 2
5. Jerk 5 × 2
6. Hanging knees to chest 2 × 10–15

## WEEK TWO

### Mon (Light)

1. General warm-up 10–15 mins
2. Back squat 5 × 3
3. Power snatch from blocks or dead hang power snatch 5 × 2
4. Power clean from blocks or dead hang power clean 5 × 2
5. Bench press or incline press 5 × 5
6. Dumbbell hammer curl 3 × 6–8
7. Bent-legged sit-up 2–3 × 8–12

### Thurs (Medium)

1. General warm-up 10–15 mins
2. Front squat 5 × 2
3. Military press or incline press 5 × 2, 5 × 3, or 5 × 5
4. Trap Bar deadlift 5 × 3 or 5 × 5
5. EZ Bar curl or Log Bar curl 3 × 6–8
6. Plank (1–2 sets), and side plank (1 set per side)

# PROGRAM NO. 8

Program No. 8 is a three-day per week program that includes two athletic strength training sessions and one day of circuit training for cardio fitness. This is a good program for lifters who want to train more often than twice a week, but find that they get too sore and stiff if they do squats, pulling exercises and overhead work more often than twice a week.

I've arranged the circuit training part of the program to fit a typical home gym situation where you have relatively limited equipment. If you train at a commercial gym and have more equipment available, you can add different exercises as desired.

Don't go too heavy when you do the circuit training. Keep the weights in the light to medium range, and make it a cardio session. Do each rep in smooth, steady, perfect form—don't rush the reps or start bouncing the bar up and down!—but try to move to the next exercise as fast as possible. (Obviously, you will set up all of your equipment before you begin the circuit.)

If you prefer to simply take a conventional cardio workout on Wednesday, in lieu of the circuit training program, that's fine. Another alternative would be to use Dr. Ken's "carrying stuff" program for your Wednesday workout.

This program works very well when combined with a simple cycling system.

On your strength training days, start light on each exercise and do a series of progressively heavier sets, finishing with your top weight for the day.

**Mon**

1. General warm-up 10–15 mins
2. Power snatch 3 × 3, 3 × 2, 2 × 1
3. Snatch grip high pull 3 × 2
4. Push press 5 × 2
5. Front squat 5 × 3 or 5 × 2
6. Bent-legged sit-up 2 × 8–12

**Wed**

1. General warm-up 10–15 mins
2. Repeat the following circuit 3–5 times:
   a. Light back squat 10 reps
   b. Barbell bent-over rowing 10 reps
   c. Military press or alternate dumbbell press 10 reps
   d. Hammer curl 10 reps
   e. Hanging knees to chest 10–15 reps
3. Repeat the following circuit 3–5 times:
   a. Bent-legged deadlift or Trap Bar deadlift with light weight 10 reps
   b. Front raise with barbell plate 10 reps
   c. Reverse curl or alternate dumbbell curl 10 reps
   d. Jump rope 1–2 mins
   e. Sledge hammer tire smash 10 times on each side

**Fri**

1. General warm-up 10–15 mins
2. Power clean 3 × 3, 3 × 2, 2 × 1
3. Clean grip high pull 3 × 2
4. Military press or incline press 5 × 3
5. Back squat or Trap Bar deadlift 5 × 3 or 5 × 2
6. One dumbbell side bend 2 × 8–12 per side

# PROGRAM NO. 9

Program No. 9 is a two-day per week program with limited volume. It's a good program for older trainees with limited energy. It's also a good program for lifters who have trouble recovering from their workouts, or who need extra days of rest to avoid excessive soreness or stiffness in their joints.

This is the sort of program that works well for lifters age 50 and up—although younger men (like those young guys in their forties!) may find that it works very well for them, too.

As with the other programs in this chapter, using a simple cycling system would be an excellent idea.

On each exercise, start light and add weight on each set. Finish with one set using your top weight for the day.

**Mon**

1. General warm-up 10–15 mins
2. Power snatch 2 × 3, 2 × 2, 1 × 1
3. Push press 3 × 2
4. Front squat 3 × 2
5. Bent-legged sit-up 2 × 8–12

**Thurs**

1. General warm-up 10–15 mins
2. Power clean 2 × 3, 2 × 2, 1 × 1
3. Jerk 4 × 1
4. Back squat or Trap Bar deadlift 5 × 2–3
5. Hanging knees to chest 2 × 10–15

# PROGRAM NO. 10

Program No. 10 is another two-day per week program with reduced volume. Older lifters will probably do better on a program with this level of volume than on a program with higher volume.

This program will include a total of four different workouts to be used over a period of two weeks.

Use a simple cycling system for best results with this program!

On each exercise, start light and add weight on each set. Do the final set with your top weight for the day.

## Week One

### Mon

1. General warm-up 10–15 mins
2. Power snatch 3 × 2, 3 × 1
3. Back squat 5 × 3
4. Hanging knees to chest 2 × 10–15

### Thurs

1. General warm-up 10–15 mins
2. Power clean 3 × 2, 3 × 1
3. Push press or jerk 3 × 2, 3 × 1
4. Plank (1–2 sets), and side plank (1 set per side)

## Week Two

**Mon**

1. General warm-up 10–15 mins
2. Snatch grip high pull 5 × 2
3. Incline press 5 × 3
4. Front squat 5 × 2
5. Bent-legged sit-up 2 × 8–12

**Thurs**

1. General warm-up 10–15 mins
2. Clean grip high pull 5 × 2
3. Military press, push press or jerk 3 × 2, 2 × 1
4. Trap Bar deadlift 5 × 2 or 5 × 3
5. Plank (1–2 sets), and side plank (1 set per side)

# 18

---

# TEN BASIC STRENGTH TRAINING
# PROGRAMS FOR OLDER LIFTERS

The training programs in this chapter are designed for older lifters who are interested in serious strength training, but who don't use athletic strength training movements or don't have the equipment to perform them, such as rubber bumper plates and a lifting platform. These lifters prefer to base their training programs on basic but highly effective strength-building movements such as back squats, front squats, military presses, bench presses, incline presses, bent-legged deadlifts, Trap Bar deadlifts, and barbell bent-over rowing.

If you're an older lifter who falls into this category—and there are quite a few of you out there!—you're really going to enjoy the programs in this chapter.

As with the athletic strength training programs in the previous chapter, the programs in this chapter are all low-volume programs. They use the divided workout principle, and they're variations of the abbreviated training programs that so many of us have used with great success in our training.

The programs can be performed with basic equipment, and are well suited to cellar-dwellers and garage gorillas. They also can be performed in almost any serious commercial gym—serious being defined as a gym where you can perform squats and deadlifts without a pencil-necked personal trainer having a coronary about it because you're "scaring the other members!" (You know what I mean.)

If you have difficulty recovering from any of the workouts, reduce the workload or take an extra day of rest in-between training sessions. Doing less work is almost always a good idea. Doing more work is rarely a good idea for older lifters.

On any of the programs, use a basic cycling system. Older lifters tend to over-estimate how heavy they can train and how often they can take a heavy workout. A sensible cycling system helps keep you from going too heavy too often.

The four week 70%–80–%–90%–95–100% cycling system works well with any of these programs. So does a six or eight-week cycle, provided you do the majority of your training in the 80–85% range, which is typically the most productive training range for an older lifter.

For example, you might try the following for an eight-week cycle:

Week One—70%
Week Two—80%
Week Three—80%
Week Four—85%
Week Five—85%
Week Six—90%
Week Seven—95%
Week Eight—100%

Another simple option would be to use a four-week cycle where you use 70%, 75%, 80% and 85%. At the end of four weeks, begin a new cycle, using the same program or a different program. After two or three cycles, push into 90–100% territory to finish your cycle.

Remember, as an older lifter, the key to success is consistent, regular, intelligent training. You need to work hard, but not so hard that you end up impossibly stiff, sore and tired. Slow and steady is best.

## PROGRAM NO. 11

Program No. 11 is a three-day per week divided workout program. You'll do two barbell exercises and one gut exercise in each session. Each workout involves a total of ten sets of barbell work.

On each exercise, start light and add weight on each set. On each of your barbell exercises, you'll perform four progressively heavier sets, followed by one set with your top weight for the day.

Remember to use a simple cycling program for best results on this program!

**Tues**

1. General warm-up 10–15 mins
2. Back squat or front squat 5 × 5, 5 × 3, 5 × 2 or 5/4/3/2/1
3. Barbell curl, reverse curl, Log Bar curl or hammer curl with dumbbells 5 × 5
4. Bent-legged sit-up 2–3 × 8–12

**Thurs**

1. Bench press or incline press 5 × 5, 5 × 3, 5 × 2, or 5/4/3/2/1
2. Barbell bent-over rowing or lat machine pull-downs to the chest 5 × 5
3. Plank (1–2 sets), and side plank (1 set to each side)

**Sat**

1. Bent-legged deadlift or Trap Bar deadlift 5 × 5, 5 × 3, 5 × 2 or 5/4/3/2/1
2. Military press 5 × 5, 5 × 3, or 5 × 2 or 5/4/3/2/1 or
   Alternate dumbbell press 5 × 5 per arm
3. Hanging knees to chest 2 × 10–15

## PROGRAM NO. 12

Program No. 12 is a two-day per week divided workout program. Training twice a week may work better for some of you due to the increased number of off days.

You also can try two strength training workouts per week and one cardio session. Just be sure not to go too hard or too long on your cardio training day.

For greater variety and a more balanced program, I'm going to give you a two-week program with four different workouts.

For each of your barbell and dumbbell exercises, start light and add weight on each set, working up to one set with your top weight.

For best results, use a simple cycling program. If nothing else, train heavy for two weeks, then drop back and take a light to medium week—and then repeat the three-week cycle.

## Week One

**Tues**

1. General warm-up 10–15 mins
2. Back squat 5 × 5, 5 × 3 or 5/4/3/2/1
3. Bench press 5 × 5, 5 × 3, or 5/4/3/2/1
4. Barbell bent-over row or pull-downs to the chest 3 × 5–6
5. Front raise with barbell plate 2 × 10–12
6. Plank (1–2 sets) and side plank (1 set per side)

**Fri**

1. General warm-up 10–15 mins
2. Trap Bar deadlift 5 × 5, 5 × 3, 5 × 2 or 5/4/3/2/1
3. Military press 5 × 5, 5 × 3, 5 × 2 or 5/4/3/2/1
4. Hammer curl with dumbbells or Log Bar 3 × 5–6
5. Dumbbell side bend 2 × 12–15 per side

## WEEK TWO

**Tues**

1. General warm-up 10–15 mins
2. Front squat 5 × 5, 5 × 3, 5 × 2 or 5/4/3/2/1
3. Dumbbell bench press or dumbbell incline press
   3 × 8–10

   or

   One-arm dumbbell bench press or one-arm dumbbell incline press 3 × 8–10 per arm

*Note:* Any of these can be performed to good effect on a heavy-duty stability ball.

4. Lateral raise 2 × 8–10
5. One-arm dumbbell row 3 × 8–10 per arm
6. Bent-legged sit-up 2 × 8–12

**Fri**

1. General warm-up 10–15 mins
2. Trap Bar deadlift 5 × 5, 5 × 3, 5 × 2 or 5/4/3/2/1
3. Alternate dumbbell press 5 × 5–6 per arm
4. EZ bar curl or alternate dumbbell curl 3 × 6–8
5. Hanging knees to chest 2 × 10–15

# PROGRAM NO. 13

Program No. 13 features two strength training days and one day of circuit training for extra cardiovascular conditioning. Be sure not to go too hard or too heavy on your circuit training. The idea is to make it a "cardio training with weights" day, not a strength and muscle building day.

The program covers two weeks, and gives you six different workouts. For best results, follow a simple cycling program where you use 70% for the first two weeks, and then go up to 75–80% for the next two weeks, and so on.

**WEEK ONE**

**Mon**

1. General warm-up 10–15 mins
2. Back squat 5 × 5, 5 × 3, or 5/4/3/2/1
3. Bench press or incline press 5 × 5, 5 × 3, or 5/4/3/2/1
4. Bent-legged sit-up 2 × 8–12

**Wed**

1. General warm-up 10–15 mins
2. Circuit training: perform the following circuit 3–5 times
   a. Dumbbell curl and press 6–8 reps
   b. Trap Bar deadlift (light!) 8–10 reps
   c. Dumbbell bench press or dumbbell incline press 6–8 reps
   d. Hanging knees to chest 10 reps
   e. Jump rope 1–2 mins
3. Circuit training: perform the following circuit 3–5 times:
   a. Pushups or pushups with feet on bench 10–25 reps
   b. Barbell bent-over row 6–8 reps
   c. Alternate front raise with dumbbells 8–10 reps per arm
   d. Back squat (light!) 8–10 reps
   e. Barbell reverse curl 6–8 reps

*Note:* if two circuits is too much training for you, then just do one circuit—or do two circuits, but work through each circuit two times for a total of four circuits during your workout.

**Fri**

1. General warm-up 10–15 mins
2. Trap Bar deadlift 5 × 5, 5 × 3, 5 × 2 or 5/4/3/2/1
3. Military press 5 × 5, 5 × 3, 5 × 2 or 5/4/3/2/1
4. Plank (1–2 sets), and side plank (1 set per side)

## Week Two

### Mon

1. General warm-up 10–15 mins
2. Front squat 5 × 5, 5 × 3, or 5/4/3/2/1
3. Dumbbell bench press or incline dumbbell press 5 × 5–10
4. Bent-legged sit-up 2 × 8–12

### Wed

1. General warm-up 10–15 mins
2. Circuit training—perform the following circuit 3–5 times:
   a. Jump rope 1–2 mins
   b. Plank 30–60 seconds
   c. Hammer curl 6–8 reps
   d. Back or front squat (light!) 5–10 reps
   e. One-arm dumbbell row 6–8 reps per arm
3. Circuit training—perform the following circuit 3–5 times:
   a. Barbell curl 6–8 reps
   b. Military press 10–12 reps
   c. Bent-over row 10–12 reps
   d. Trap Bar shrug (light!) 10–12 reps
   e. Back squat (light!) 10–12 reps

*Note:* if two circuits is too much training for you, then just do one circuit—or do two circuits, but work through each circuit two times for a total of four circuits during your workout.

### Fri

1. General warm-up 10–15 mins
2. Trap Bar deadlift 5 × 5, 5 × 3, 5 × 2 or 5/4/3/2/1
3. Military press 5 × 5, 5 × 3, 5 × 2 or 5/4/3/2/1
4. Hanging knees to chest 2 × 10–15

221

## PROGRAM NO. 14

Program No. 14 is a low-volume, three-day per week program that focuses on three primary exercises. You perform only one barbell exercise in each workout, followed by two or three sets of gut work. It doesn't sound like very much work, and it's not—but it's a very effective training program for older lifters.

I've used this program in the past, and had great success with it. So don't let its simplicity fool you. This is a really good program for older lifters.

As with the other programs, Program No. 14 works very well when combined with a simple cycling system.

**Mon**

1.  General warm-up 10–15 mins
2.  Back squat or front squat 5–7 progressively heavier sets of 5, 3 or 2 reps, working up to your top weight for the day.
3.  Hanging knees to chest 2 × 10–15

**Wed**

1.  General warm-up 10–15 mins
2.  Bench press, incline press, or military press 5–7 progressively heavier sets of 5, 3 or 2 reps, working up to your top weight for the day.
3.  Bent-legged sit-up 2 × 8–12

**Fri**

1.  General warm-up 10–15 mins
2.  Bent-legged deadlift or Trap Bar deadlift 5–7 progressively heavier sets of 5, 3 or 2 reps, working up to your top weight for the day.
3.  Dumbbell side-bend 2 × 10–15 reps per side

# PROGRAM NO. 15

Program No. 15 is similar to Program No. 14, but it extends over a two-week period. You do six different workouts, using a different barbell exercise in each workout. This program gives you plenty of variety, and plenty of time for recovery and recuperation, since you'll only perform any particular exercise once every two weeks.

Note that you'll perform your heaviest movements—squats and deadlifts—on Monday of each week. On this schedule, your lower back, hips and knees should feel strong and well rested whenever you train your squats or deadlifts.

This program would work best if you followed a simple cycling system adapted to a two-week training schedule. For example, weeks one and two might be 70% weeks, and weeks two and three might be 75% or 80% weeks.

## WEEK ONE

### Mon

1. General warm-up 10–15 mins
2. Back squat or front squat 5–7 progressively heavier sets of 5, 3 or 2 reps, working up to your top weight for the day.
3. Hanging knees to chest 2 × 10–15

### Wed

1. General warm-up 10–15 mins
2. Bench press or incline press 5–7 progressively heavier sets of 5, 3 or 2 reps, working up to your top weight for the day.
3. Bent-legged sit-up 2 × 8–12

223

**Fri**

1. General warm-up 10–15 mins
2. Barbell bent-over row 5–7 progressively heavier sets of 5 reps, working up to your top weight for the day.
3. Dumbbell side bend 2 × 10–15 per side

## Week Two

**Mon**

1. General warm-up 10–15 mins
2. Bent-legged deadlift or Trap Bar deadlift 5–7 progressively heavier sets of 5, 3 or 2 reps, working up to your top weight for the day.
3. Hanging knees to chest 2 × 10–15

**Wed**

1. General warm-up 10–15 mins
2. Incline or military press 5–7 progressively heavier sets of 5, 3, or 2 reps, working up to your top weight for the day.
3. Plank (1–2 sets), and side plank (1 set per side)

**Fri**

1. General warm-up 10–15 mins
2. EZ bar curl, Log Bar curl or dumbbell hammer curl 5 progressively heavier sets of 5 reps, working up to your top weight for the day.
3. Bent-legged sit-up 2 × 8–12

# PROGRAM NO. 16

Program No. 14 is another two day per week program. You'll use four different workouts over a two-week period, and train each exercise once every two weeks. This schedule will allow maximum time for recovery and recuperation.

Be sure to follow a simple cycling system with this program. Since it is a two-week schedule, your cycling system should be based on two-week intervals. For example, weeks one and two would be 70% weeks, and weeks two and three would be 75% or 80% weeks.

### WEEK ONE

**Tues**

1. General warm-up 10–15 mins
2. Back squat or front squat 5–7 progressively heavier sets of 5, 3, or 2 reps, working up to your top weight for the day.
3. EZ Bar curl 4–5 progressively heavier sets of 5 reps, working up to your top weight for the day.
4. Bent-legged sit-up 2 × 8–12

**Fri**

1. General warm-up 10–15 mins
2. Bench press or incline press 5–7 progressively heavier sets of 5, 3, or 2 reps, working up to your top weight for the day.
3. Barbell bent-over rowing 5–7 progressively heavier sets of 5 reps, working up to your top weight for the day.
4. Hanging knees to chest 2 × 10–15

## WEEK TWO

**Tues**

1. General warm-up 10–15 mins
2. Trap Bar deadlift 5–7 progressively heavier sets of 5, 3, or 2 reps, working up to your top weight for the day.
3. Front raise with barbell plate 2–3 × 8–10
4. Dumbbell side bend 2 × 10–15 per side

**Fri**

1. General warm-up 10–15 mins
2. Military press 5–7 progressively heavier sets of 5, 3, or 2 reps, working up to your top weight for the day.
3. Lat machine pull-down to chest or one-arm dumbbell rowing 5 × 5 progressively heavier sets, working up to your top weight for the day.
4. Plank (1–2 sets), and side plank (1 set per side)

## PROGRAM NO. 17

In Program No. 17, you train three times per week, alternating strength training workouts and cardio training. In week one, you perform two strength training workouts and two cardio workouts. In week two, you do the reverse.

On each exercise, start light and add weight on each set, working up to your top weight for the day.

Use a simple cycling system on this program! Schedule it over two week intervals, i.e., weeks one and two—70%, weeks two and three, 80%, etc.

### WEEK ONE

**Mon**

1. General warm-up 10–15 mins
2. Back squat 5 × 5, 1 × 3, 1 × 1
3. Bench press or incline press 5 × 5, 1 × 3, 1 × 1
4. Bent-legged sit-up 2 × 8–12

**Wed**

1. General warm-up 10–15 mins
2. Dr. Ken's "carrying stuff" cardio workout—30 to 45 minutes.

**Fri**

1. General warm-up 10–15 mins
2. Trap Bar deadlift 5 × 5, 1 × 3, 1 × 1
3. Barbell bent-over row 5 × 5
4. Hanging knees to chest 2 × 10–15

## WEEK TWO

**Mon**

1. General warm-up 10–15 mins
2. Dr. Ken's "carrying stuff" cardio workout—30–45 mins
3. Bent-legged sit-up 2–3 × 8–12

**Wed**

1. General warm-up 10–15 mins
2. Back squat 5 × 5 or 5 × 3
3. Bench press or incline press 5 × 5 or 5 × 3
4. Trap Bar deadlift 5 × 5 or 5 × 3

**Fri**

1. General warm-up 10–15 mins
2. Dr. Ken's "carrying stuff" cardio workout—30–45 mins
3. Hanging knees to chest 2 × 10–15

## PROGRAM NO. 18

Program No. 18 is a four-day per week program, with two strength training workouts and two cardio workouts. If the program is too tiring, then switch to an every other day schedule or a three-day per week program similar to Program No. 17.

Be sure to use a simple cycling program on this schedule!

**Mon**

1. General warm-up 10–15 mins
2. Back squat 5 × 5, 1 × 3, 1 × 1
3. Bench press 5 × 5, 1 × 3, 1 × 1
4. EZ bar curl 4 × 5
5. Hanging knees to chest 2 × 10–15

**Tues**

1. General warm-up 10–15 mins
2. Any cardio exercise of your choice for 15—30 mins
   or
   Dr. Ken's "carrying stuff" cardio workout—30—45 mins

**Thurs**

1. General warm-up 10–15 mins
2. Trap Bar deadlift 5 × 5, 1 × 3, 1 × 1
3. Incline press or military press 5 × 5, 5 × 3 or 5 × 2
4. Barbell bent-over row 4 × 5
5. Bent-legged sit-up 2 × 8–12

**Fri**

1. General warm-up 10–15 mins
2. Any cardio exercise of your choice for 15—30 mins
   or
   Dr. Ken's "carrying stuff" cardio workout—30—45 mins

## PROGRAM NO. 19

Program No. 19 is a four-day per week divided workout schedule. You'll do three strength training days and one cardio day each week. You'll hit different exercises in each of your strength training workouts.

You'll do your first strength training session on Monday, followed by your cardio workout on Tuesday. You'll rest on Wednesday, train on Thursday, rest on Friday, train on Saturday and rest on Sunday. So Tuesday (your cardio day) is the only day when you'll be training immediately after a previous workout day.

This program would work very well with a simple cycling system.

**Mon**

1. General warm-up 10–15 mins
2. Back squat 5–7 progressively heavier sets of 5 reps, working up to your top weight for the day.
3. EZ bar curl 4 × 5
4. Hanging knees to chest 2 × 10–15

**Tues**

1. General warm-up 10–15 mins
2. Any cardio exercise of your choice for 15–30 mins
   or
   Dr. Ken's "carrying stuff" cardio workout—30–45 mins

**Thurs**

1. General warm-up 10–15 mins
2. Trap Bar deadlift 5–7 progressively heavier sets of 5 reps, working up to your top weight for the day.
3. Close grip bench press 4 × 5

   or

   Military press 5 × 5, 5 × 3, 5 × 2 or 5/4/3/2/1

   or

   Alternate dumbbell press 5 × 5–6 reps per arm
4. Dumbbell side bend 2 × 10–15

**Sat**

1. General warm-up 10–15 mins
2. Bench press or incline press 5–7 progressively heavier sets of five reps, working up to your top weight for the day.
3. Barbell bent-over rowing or pull-downs 5 progressively heavier sets of 5 reps, working up to your top weight for the day.
4. Bent-legged sit-up 2 × 8–12

## PROGRAM NO. 20

Here's a two-day per week program where you do one day of strength training per week and one day of cardio training. This is an ideal program for older lifters with low energy reserves, or those who find they have trouble with soreness and stiffness if they train too often. I know it doesn't look like much on paper, but in terms of results it can be hugely effective. For many readers, especially those over the age of 50, this could very well be the best program they try.

This is a two-week program. You'll do squats in week one and deadlifts in week two.

This program would work well with a simple cycling system where you use the same percentages in each two-week period, e.g., 70% for weeks one and two, 80% for weeks three and four, etc.

### WEEK ONE

**Tues**

1.  General warm-up 10–15 mins
2.  Back squat or front squat 5–7 progressively heavier sets of 3–5 reps, working up to your top weight for the day.
3.  Bench press, incline press or military press 5/4/3/2/1
4.  EZ bar curl 2–3 × 5–6
5.  Hanging knees to chest 1 × 10–15
    or
    Dumbbell side-bend 1 × 10–15 per side

## Thurs or Fri

1. General warm-up 10–15 mins
2. Any cardio exercise of your choice for 15–30 mins
   or
   Dr. Ken's "carrying stuff" cardio workout—30–45 mins
3. Plank 1–2 sets

### WEEK TWO

## Tues

1. General warm-up 10–15 mins
2. Bent-legged deadlift or Trap Bar deadlift 5–7 progressively heavier sets of 3–5 reps, working up to your top weight for the day.
3. Bench press, incline press or military press 5/4/3/2/1
   or
   Alternate dumbbell press 3–5 × 5–6 reps per arm
4. Barbell bent-over rowing or pull-down to chest
   3 × 5–6
5. Bent-legged sit–up 1 × 8–12

## Thurs or Fri

1. General warm-up 10–15 mins
2. Any cardio exercise of your choice for 15–30 mins
   or
   Dr. Ken's "carrying stuff" cardio workout—30–45 mins
3. Plank (1 set), and side plank (1 set for each side)

# 19

---

# TEN TOTAL BODY WORKOUTS
# FOR OLDER LIFTERS

I got started in weight training in the late 1960's—right about the time that the muscle comics of the era were touting the alleged benefits of five-day a week training programs, six-day per week programs, and the infamous six-day double-split routine.

We were told that the only way to become a "champion"—i.e., "one of the guys in the supplement ads"—was to train two to four hours five or six days per week.

I tried it. So did you. We all tried it.

And it didn't work.

In fact, it was such a colossal failure that it destroyed many training careers before they even got started.

A very small percentage of trainees somehow got beyond the mainstream silliness. But it was always a near thing. I escaped the muscle mag insanity only because I discovered the writing of a man named Bradley J. Steiner—who promoted something strange, radical and revolutionary: training just three times a week on total body workouts that lasted about an hour.

Steiner's articles got me back on the path to training sanity—and training success—in short order. And they did the same for plenty of other guys around the world. They may very well have been what worked for you—and for many other readers of this book.

For that, we owe Bradley J. Steiner an enormous debt—and a very big collective "thank you!"

But that's not all we have to thank him for.

As older trainees, many of us will do no better than to train on the type of programs that Brad Steiner advocated way back in the swinging 60's. And that's particularly true for those readers who are over the age of sixty.

Let me repeat that—because it's a very important point. The programs in this chapter may be the very best programs in this book for those of you who are over the age of sixty.

Why are Steiner's programs so valuable for older lifters?

There are several reasons.

First, Steiner's three-day per week, total body training programs featured basic exercises that could be performed in any modestly equipped home gym. All you needed was an ordinary barbell and dumbbell set (not an Olympic bar), a flat bench and a set of squat stands. Steiner himself trained for several years in a small apartment in New York City with exactly that sort of set-up.

Second, Steiner's programs are extremely well-balanced. They allow you to work your entire body from head to toe. You end up building a body that is strong and well developed all over. No weak links. No joints or muscle groups that aren't getting enough attention. No "injuries waiting to happen." Plus, hitting each major muscle group three times per week will help you keep your entire body flexible and supple.

Third, the workload in Steiner's programs is rigorously controlled. You don't run the risk of doing too many exercises, too many sets or too many reps. You also avoid the risk of over-training a particular exercise or a particular joint, and ending up with some sort of repetitive motion injury. In Steiner's programs, you typically perform two or three sets of any particular exercise. On occasion, you may perform four or even five sets of a major movement, such as squats, deadlifts or bench presses. But the over-all stress on any particular body-part is greatly reduced when you follow one of Steiner's programs.

Fourth, Steiner's programs offer an easy way to balance training for strength and power, training for muscular development and training for cardiovascular fitness and overall "conditioning."

Fifth, Steiner's programs offer enough variety to keep things interesting. Because you train your entire body in each workout, you do a variety of different exercises. Many trainees enjoy this approach more than the limited exercise, abbreviated training programs outlined in earlier chapters.

Finally, Steiner's programs allow you to train hard, but not TOO hard—and heavy, but not TOO heavy. They're not weight-lifting programs, and they're not powerlifting programs. They're weight training programs—and they're very good ones.

## PROGRAM NO. 21

Program No. 21 is a classic three-day per week program that builds a great balance of strength, muscle and fitness. It requires only limited equipment, and that makes it a sure-fire winner for cellar-dwellers and garage gorillas. And you can complete it in under an hour.

Older lifters may find that they do best on this program—or on any of the programs in this chapter—if they follow a simple cycling system or if they use the heavy/medium/light system, i.e., one heavy workout each week, one medium workout and one light workout. And remember—for an older lifter, "heavy" doesn't mean 100% of your max. It may be no more than 80%, 85% or 90% of your max. So you may do 70% on Monday (your light day), 80% on Wednesday (your medium day), and 90% on Friday (your heavy day).

If three workouts per week are too tiring, try two workouts per week. You can do light cardio on the third day in place of your weight training session, or you can just relax, recover and recuperate.

### Mon/Wed/Fri

1. General warm-up 10–15 mins
2. Alternate front raise 2 × 10–12
3. Barbell curl or alternate dumbbell curl 2 × 6–8
4. Military press or alternate dumbbell press 2 × 8–10
5. Back squat 1 × 12, 1 × 10, 1 × 8
6. Breathing pullover with very light dumbbells after each set of squats 3 × 15–20
7. Bench press or incline dumbbell bench press 2 × 8–10
8. Barbell bent-over row, pull-down to chest or one-arm dumbbell row 2 × 8–10

9. Bent-legged deadlift or Trap Bar deadlift 1 × 10–15 or 2 × 8–10
10. Bent-legged sit-up 2 × 8–12

## PROGRAM NO. 22

Program No. 22 is another three-day per week, total body training program. As with the previous program, this workout includes several dumbbell exercises. Many older lifters will find that dumbbell exercises are easier on their joints and more forgiving than comparable barbell movements.

**Mon/Wed/Fri**

1. General warm-up 10–15 mins
2. Alternate dumbbell curl 2 × 6–8
3. Alternate dumbbell press 3 × 6–8
4. Back squat or front squat 4 × 5–6
5. Dumbbell incline press or dumbbell bench press 3 × 6–8

   or

   One-arm incline dumbbell press or one-arm dumbbell bench press 3 × 6–8 per arm

*Note:* These can be performed on a heavy-duty stability ball.

6. One-arm dumbbell rowing 3 × 8–10 per arm
7. Alternate front raise 2 × 8–10 per arm
8. Bent-legged or Trap Bar deadlift 4 × 5
9. Dumbbell side bend 2 × 10–15 per side on Monday

   or

   Bent-legged sit-up 2 × 8–12 on Wednesday

   or

   Lying leg raise 2 × 15–20 or hanging knees to chest 2 × 10–15 on Friday

# PROGRAM NO. 23

Here's another three-day per week, total body program that combines barbell and dumbbell exercises. This one also includes some rope skipping and power cleans for greater conditioning value. Steiner was a big advocate of both rope skipping drills and weightlifting (athletic strength training) used in combination with basic barbell and dumbbell training. If the rope skipping causes foot or ankle problems, substitute five or ten minutes on a stationary bicycle or step machine, or do several minutes of step-ups (without weight) onto a low bench or other sturdy platform.

## Mon/Wed/Fri

1. General warm-up 10–15 mins
2. Power clean 4 × 3–5 or Trap Bar deadlift 4 × 5
3. Jump rope 1–2 × 1–2 mins or do other light cardio work for 5–10 mins
4. Dumbbell press 2 × 8–10
5. Dumbbell hammer curl 2 × 6–8
6. Back squat 1 × 12, 1 × 10, 1 × 8
7. Dumbbell bench press or incline dumbbell press 2 × 8–10

   or

   One-arm dumbbell bench press or one-arm incline dumbbell press 2 × 8–10 per arm

*Note:* These can be performed on a heavy-duty stability ball.

8. Barbell bent-over rowing or pull-down to chest 3 × 6–8
9. Alternate front raise with dumbbells 2 × 8–10
10. Close grip bench press 2 × 8–10
11. Bent-legged sit-up 2 × 8–12
12. One dumbbell side-bend 2 × 10–15 per side

## PROGRAM NO. 24

This program combines barbell and dumbbell training two times per week with one day where you do rope skipping or other cardio training combined with Dr. Ken's "carrying stuff" cardio workout. This is an excellent all-around program for older lifters.

If you wish, add a few sets of some light barbell and dumbbell exercises (e.g., alternate front raises, close grip bench presses, barbell or dumbbell curls, dumbbell hammer curls, reverse curls, prone hyperextensions, neck work with a head-strap, grip work or gut work) to the Wednesday session before you begin your lugging and loading work.

Also, note that you can alternate medium and heavy days on Monday and Friday, when you do your strength training work, and also, that you can use a simple cycling program to good effect on this schedule.

**Mon/Fri**

1. General warm-up 10–15 mins
2. Military press 4 × 5
3. Back squat or front squat 4 × 3–5
4. Barbell or dumbbell bench press or incline press 4 × 5
5. Barbell bent-over row 4 × 5
6. Trap-Bar deadlift 4 × 3–5
7. Bent-legged sit-up 2 × 8–12
   or
   Hanging knees to chest 2 × 10–15

**Wed**

1. General warm-up 10–15 mins
2. Jump-rope 3 × 1–2 mins or other light cardio for 5–10 mins
3. Dr. Ken's "carrying stuff" cardio workout—30–45 mins

## PROGRAM NO. 25

Program No. 25 gives you three total-body workouts each week—but each workout features different exercises, different sets and different reps. It provides plenty of variety, builds a well-balanced physique, and helps assure that you don't over-do any single exercise or over-stress any particular muscle or joint. This is another very good program for older lifters.

Use a simple cycling system for best results on this schedule.

**Mon**

1. General warm-up 10–15 mins
2. Jump rope 2 × 2 mins or other light cardio work 5–10 mins
3. Alternate dumbbell press 2–3 × 6–8 per arm
4. Reverse curl 2–3 × 6–8
5. Front squat 3–4 × 5
6. Dumbbell incline press 2 × 10–12
7. Barbell bent-over row 3 × 10–12
8. Trap Bar deadlift 2 × 12/10
9. Bent-legged sit-up 2 × 8–12

**Wed**

1. General warm-up 10–15 mins
2. Power clean and press 4 × 3–5

*Note:* If you prefer, do military presses 4 × 3–5.

3. Dumbbell hammer curl 2 × 10–12
4. Back squat 3 × 15/12/10
5. Breathing pullover after each set of squats 3 × 15–20
6. Pushups or pushups with feet on bench 2–3 × 10–25
7. Jump rope 2 × 2 mins or other light cardio work for 5–10 mins
8. Alternate front raise with dumbbells 2 × 10–12 per arm
9. One dumbbell side bend 2 × 10–15 per side

**Fri**

1. General warm-up 10–15 mins
2. Power snatch 4–5 × 3

*Note:* If you prefer, do upright rowing or shoulder shrugs 2 × 8–10.

3. Trap Bar deadlift 4 × 3–5
4. Barbell bench press 4 × 5–6
5. One-arm dumbbell rowing 3 × 8–10 per arm
6. Close grip bench press 3 × 6–8
7. EZ bar curl 3 × 6–8
8. Dumbbell lateral raise 2 × 8–10
9. Jump rope 2 × 2 mins
10. Lying leg raise 2 × 12–15 or hanging knees to chest 2 × 10–15

## PROGRAM NO. 26

Program No. 26 is a simple, no frills, three-day per week total body training program. This schedule would work very well when combined with a simple cycling system, such as a four-week 70%–80%–90%–95–100% schedule.

If time and energy permit, do some light cardio work two or three times per week. But make it light and easy—don't overdo things! Your cardio program might be as easy as going for a two or three mile walk.

**Mon/Wed/Fri**

1. General warm-up 10–15 mins
2. Military press 3 × 5–6
3. EZ bar curl 2 × 10–12 or 3 × 5–6
4. Back squat 2 × 10–12 or front squat 4 × 5
5. Bench press or incline dumbbell press 3 × 6–8
6. Barbell bent-over rowing 3 × 6–8 or 2 × 10–12
7. Alternate front raise with dumbbells 2 × 10–12 per arm
8. Dumbbell lateral raise 2 × 10–12
9. Pushup or pushup with feet on bench 2 × 10–25
10. Bent-legged deadlift or Trap Bar deadlift 2 × 10–12 or 4 × 5
11. Bent-legged sit-up 2 × 8–12
12. Plank (1–2 sets) and side plank (1 set per side)

## PROGRAM NO. 27

Program No. 27 is another three-day per week program, with similar, but slightly different workouts each time you train. This one focuses on athletic strength exercises (which Steiner often included in his programs), but includes a variety of other movements. It gives you an excellent workout, with a near-perfect balance of strength and power training, muscle building, and conditioning for an older lifter. If you can perform power cleans, power snatches, and push presses, give this program a try.

This program would work best if you followed a simple cycling system, such as the four-week 70%–80%–90%–95–100% system.

On each exercise, start light, and work up in weight from set to set, finishing with your top weight for the day.

**Mon**

1. General warm-up 10–15 mins
2. Power snatch 5 × 2
3. Military press 5 × 3
4. Front squat 5 × 3
5. Bench press 5 × 3
6. EZ bar curl 3 × 5–6
7. Hanging knees to chest 2 × 10–15

**Wed**

1. General warm-up 10–15 mins
2. Power clean 5 × 2
3. Push press 5 × 2
4. Back squat 5 × 2
5. Incline press 5 × 3
6. Bent-legged sit-ups 2 × 8–12

**Fri**

1. General warm-up 10–15 mins
2. Snatch grip high pull (in week one) 5 × 2
   or
   Clean grip high pull (in week two) 5 × 2
3. Incline dumbbell press 3 × 10–12
4. Trap Bar deadlift 5 × 3
5. Hammer curl with dumbbells 2 × 8–10
6. Plank (1–2 sets), and side plank (1 set per side)

## PROGRAM NO. 28

Program No. 28 is a low-volume program for lifters who have difficulty in recovering from their workouts. This is a good program if you are finding it hard to bounce back from a longer, more strenuous workout.

You may find that it helps to use the heavy/light/medium system when you train with this program. Make Monday your heavy day, Wednesday your light day, and Friday your medium day.

Alternatively, use a simple cycling system with this routine.

**Mon/Wed/Fri**

1. General warm-up 10–15 mins
2. Military press 1 × 8, 1 × 6
3. EZ bar curl 1 × 6
4. Back squat or front squat 1 × 8, 1 × 6
5. Bench press or incline press 2 × 6–8
6. Barbell bent-over row 2 × 6–8
7. Alternate front raise with dumbbells 1 × 8–10 per arm
8. Dumbbell lateral raise 1 × 8–10
9. Bent-legged deadlift or Trap Bar deadlift 2 × 8–10
10. Bent-legged sit-up 1 × 8–12

# PROGRAM NO. 29

Here's another low-volume program for lifters who have trouble recovering from their workouts. This is a very good program for lifters who are over the age of sixty. It will keep you strong and well conditioned, but it's very forgiving, and won't tire you out too badly.

For best results on this program, use a heavy/light/medium system, or a simple cycling system.

**Mon/Wed/Fri**

1. General warm-up 10–15 mins
2. Alternate dumbbell curl or alternate hammer curl 1 × 6–8 per arm
3. Alternate dumbbell press 2 × 5–6 per arm
4. Dumbbell incline press 2 × 6–8
5. One-arm dumbbell rowing 2 × 6–8 per arm
6. Back squat 1 × 12, 1 × 10
7. Bent-legged deadlift or Trap Bar deadlift 1 × 10–12
8. Alternate front raise with dumbbells 1 × 10 per arm
9. Dumbbell lateral raise 1 × 8–10
10. Reverse curl 1 × 6–8
11. Bent-legged sit-up 1 × 8–12
12. Dumbbell side bend 1 × 10–15 per side

## PROGRAM NO. 30

Program No. 30 is another classic three-day per week training program that combines barbell and dumbbell training for an excellent all-around workout. This is modeled after one of Steiner's all-time favorite programs, as detailed in his 1974 masterpiece, *A Complete Guide to Effective Barbell Training*.

Use the heavy, medium, and light system or a simple cycling system on this program.

**Mon/Wed/Fri**

1. General warm-up 10–15 mins
2. Flip snatch (Light!) 1 × 10–12 (purely for warming up purposes)
3. Seated incline bench dumbbell curl or standing alternate curl 2–3 × 6–8
4. Military press 2–3 × 5–6
5. One-arm dumbbell rowing 2–3 × 6–8 per arm
6. Incline barbell press 2–3 × 6–8
7. Back squat 2–3 × 6–8
8. Breathing pullover with light dumbbells 2–3 × 15–20 after each set of squats
9. Bent-legged deadlift or Trap Bar deadlift 2–3 × 6–8
10. Bent-legged sit-up 2–3 × 8–12

# 20

---

# TEN CIRCUIT-TRAINING PROGRAMS FOR OLDER LIFTERS

As discussed in previous chapters, older trainees need to pay attention to cardio training—but they don't need to do traditional cardio! You can get a terrific cardio workout by doing PHA or circuit training with weights. It's low impact, and highly effective, and if you're a long-time lifter, it's going to appeal to you a heck of a lot more than the idea of using a "cardio machine" for half an hour. And it's a way to be a part of Iron Game history, because you'll be following programs that date back to the 1940's and the hey-day of the York Barbell Club and the world-famous York champions.

The type of programs outlined in this chapter date back to Bob Hoffman's Simplified System of Barbell Training. In the Simplified System, the exercises were grouped in such a way that you did the first three movements with the same weight, then added weight and performed the next four movements, and then added more weight and finished with the three heaviest movements of the day. Each grouping of exercises with the same weight could be done non-stop, one exercise right after the other. So the type of circuit training outlined in this chapter has a long history and a solid connection with heavy iron and the men who lift it.

With that in mind, here are ten classic circuit-training programs for older lifters who want to combine Iron Slinging with cardio training. I've designed the programs for home gym trainees, so each circuit uses a minimum amount of equipment. I figure that most readers with home gyms have a couple of different barbells, a Trap Bar, a few different sets of dumbbells, sandbags or similar tools for lugging and loading drills, a pull-up bar, a place to do some rope skipping, and a place to do gut work. If I list an exercise that requires something you don't have, substitute another movement. The specific exercises you do are not as important as the fact that you're training circuit-style.

For your circuit-training, set all of your equipment up before you begin your first circuit, so you can move from one exercise to another without any rest. After completing your first circuit, take a one or two minute breather, and then repeat the entire circuit.

Do NOT go heavy on your exercises! This is NOT a "balls to the wall," High Intensity program where you take each set to momentary muscular failure. It's a cardio program—and the way you're training your heart and lungs is by doing a variety of different exercises with no rest between the different movements. Each exercise will work different muscle groups, but all of them will work your heart and lungs.

You can get a heck of a cardio workout by using a 95-pound barbell and going through a non-stop circuit of five or six exercises without putting the bar down. (If you don't believe me, go ahead and give Program No. 31 a try.) And if you can use several different pieces of equipment, a squat bar loaded to 135 pounds, a Trap Bar loaded to 135 pounds, and a single pair of light dumbbells is all you need for a terrific cardio workout.

Many of your cardio circuits will include athletic strength training exercises such as power snatches, power cleans and the clean and press—all performed for 12 reps. Normally, you would never dream of performing 12 reps on any of these exercises—but in this case, it's okay because you're going to be using light weights. But nevertheless, make a real effort to use good form on each rep.

On all of your circuit training exercises, move the bar smoothly and steadily. You don't need to move the bar as fast as possible. In fact, you're better off not trying to do so. Moving a light bar at a fast speed is a good way to hurt yourself.

You can do all of your training circuit-style, or you can follow a more conventional strength and power program in some of your workouts, and do circuit-training in other workouts.

You also can use circuit-training for a cardio workout after finishing your strength and power exercises.

I'll give you ten different cardio circuits. You can use any of the programs by itself or in combination with any of the other circuits.

## PROGRAM NO. 31

Here's a one-barbell cardio circuit that will knock you on your rear end if you do it right. The circuit consists of six exercises performed with the same weight on the bar. Go directly from one exercise to the next, without any rest between exercises. It's based on a training program used by multi-time UFC champion, Randy Couture, who's legitimately one of the toughest and best-conditioned men in the world—so if you think you're "too tough" for cardio training with a light barbell, think again.

This will seem really easy at first—and then it will become a little less easy—and all of a sudden it will be like arm-wrestling King Kong.

Rest one to two minutes between circuits, and repeat for a total of three to five circuits.

Note that on this or any of the other circuits you can start or finish the circuit with rope-skipping for one or two minutes.

1. Barbell curl 1 × 12
2. Military press 1 × 12
3. Barbell upright row 1 × 12
4. Barbell bent-over row 1 × 12
5. Barbell back or front squat 1 × 12
6. Bent-legged deadlift 1 × 12

# PROGRAM NO. 32

Program No. 32 is another six-exercise circuit. This one requires two barbells and a pair of dumbbells.

Begin with a light barbell and use it to perform the first four exercises with no rest between sets. Immediately move to the squat racks and use a heavier barbell (but not too heavy!) for the fifth exercise. Without resting, pick up the dumbbells and use them for your final movement.

As with the previous program, you can begin or end the circuit (or do both) with one or two minutes of rope skipping.

1. Power snatch 1 × 12
2. Barbell bent-over row 1 × 12
3. Power clean and press 1 × 12
4. Bent-legged deadlift 1 × 12
5. Back or front squat 1 × 12
6. Alternate dumbbell curl or alternate front raise
   1 × 12 per arm

## PROGRAM NO. 33

Program No. 33 is another six-exercise circuit. This one requires two barbells, a Trap Bar, and a sandbag.

Perform the first exercise with the heavier barbell, then move to the Trap Bar for your next exercise. After the Trap Bar work, use the lighter barbell for the next three exercises, and then finish up with the sandbag.

As far as weight goes, you might try 135 pounds on your squats, 135 pounds on your Trap Bar deadlifts, 65 pounds on your next group of exercises, and 50 or 60 pounds for the sandbag.

1. Back or front squat 1 × 12
2. Trap Bar deadlifts 1 × 12
3. Reverse curl 1 × 12
4. Military press 1 × 12
5. Barbell bent-over row 1 × 12
6. Sandbag shouldering exercise (like Basque stone lift to shoulder) 1 × 12 to each shoulder, alternating from one shoulder to the other
   or
   Sandbag clean and press 1 × 12–20
   or
   Sandbag curl and press

# PROGRAM NO. 34

Here's another six-exercise cardio circuit that you can perform with a single barbell. It includes bent-legged deadlifts, front squats, back squats and the clean and press, so you're going to be hitting the BIG movements in this one.

Work this program hard and fast, and you'll be surprised at how demanding it is—even if you're using a light to medium heavy weight on the bar!

1. Bent-legged deadlift 1 × 12
2. Front squat 1 × 12
3. Power clean and press 1 × 12
4. Barbell bent-over row 1 × 12
5. Barbell upright row 1 × 12
6. Back squat 1 × 12

## PROGRAM NO. 35

Program No. 35 is a single sandbag circuit-training program. I think you'll really enjoy this one. There's just something about sandbags that makes them ideal for circuit training.

As with the other programs, you don't need to go heavy. The idea is to keep moving, not to heave the heaviest sandbag you can handle. A 30 to 50 pound sandbag will be plenty heavy for this program.

1. Sandbag clean and press 1 × 12
2. Sandbag squat (with bag on right shoulder) 1 × 12
3. Pushup with sandbag on your back or with your feet on the sandbag 1 × 10–20
4. Sandbag squat (with bag on left shoulder) 1 × 12
5. Bent-over row with sandbag 1 × 12
6. Deadlift with sandbag 1 × 12

## PROGRAM NO. 36

Here's another one-barbell circuit. You begin with pushups and then go straight to the barbell movements. This one will get your heart pumping!

1. Pushups 10–25
2. Barbell clean and press 1 × 12
3. Back squat or front squat 1 × 12
4. Barbell upright row 1 × 12
5. Bent-over barbell row 1 × 12
6. Bent-legged deadlift 1 × 12

# PROGRAM NO. 37

Program No. 37 is modeled after the first course in Bob Hoffman's Simplified System of Barbell Training. You'll need three different barbells or else you'll need to make two quick weight changes as you go through the program. The weight changes are both increases, so all you need to do is slap some plates on the bar. If you have a set of squat stands, that will make things even easier.

This program doubles as a standard strength and muscle-building program, as well as a cardio training program. It's an excellent all-around program for older lifters, and is well suited for home gym trainees.

If you use the program primarily for strength and muscle-building, do one, two or three circuits. If you do two circuits, make the first circuit a light one, for warming-up purposes, and then add weight and make the next circuit more challenging. If you do three circuits, you can make the first one light, then add weight and make the next one a medium heavy circuit, and then add more weight and make the third circuit a heavy one.

For cardio conditioning, use lighter weights, keep the weights the same for each circuit, and perform three to five circuits.

If you use the program for general strength and muscle-building, add some gut work to finish things off after completing your circuits.

1. Power snatch 1 × 12
2. Barbell curl 1 × 12
3. Upright row 1 × 12
   (Weight increase of 50%.)
4. Power clean 1 × 12
5. Military press 1 × 12
6. Shoulder shrug 1 × 12
7. Barbell bent-over row 1 × 12
   (Weight increase of 50%.)
8. Front squat 1 × 12
9. Bent-legged deadlift 1 × 12
10. Back squat 1 × 12

## PROGRAM NO. 38

Program No. 38 is based on the second course in Bob Hoffman's Simplified System of Barbell Training. See the comments to program No. 37 for details on how to make maximum use of this Program.

The program works best if you have two barbells and a set of squat stands.

1. Reverse curl 1 × 12
2. Upright Row 1 × 12
3. Military press 1 × 12
   (Weight increase of 50%.)
4. Power snatch 1 × 12
5. Power clean and push press or power clean and jerk
   1 × 12
6. Barbell bent-over row 1 × 12
7. Front squat 1 × 12
   (Weight increase of 50%.)

8. Clean grip high pull 1 × 12
9. Back squat 1 × 12
10. Bent-legged deadlift 1 × 12

## PROGRAM NO. 39

Program No. 39 is another variation of the Simplified System of Barbell Training. In this variation, I'll combine some dumbbell exercises and some gut work with the barbell exercises. This makes for an extremely tough workout.

As with Programs 37 and 38, you can use heavier weights and make this a regular strength and muscle-building program, or you can use lighter weights and make it a cardio circuit. See the instructions for Programs 37 and 38.

The program works best if you can use two barbells and a set of squat stands, to avoid too many weight changes.

1. Hanging knees to chest 1 × 10–15
2. Alternate dumbbell curl 1 × 6–8 per arm
3. Alternate dumbbell press 1 × 10–12 per arm
4. Two-dumbbell power clean 1 × 12
   (Switch to barbell exercises.)
5. Power snatch 1 × 12
6. Military press 1 × 12
7. Power clean 1 × 12
8. Barbell bent-over row 1 × 12
   (Weight increase of 50%.)
9. Clean grip high pull 1 × 12
10. Back squat or front squat 1 × 12
11. Bent-legged deadlift 1 × 12
12. Bent-legged sit-up 1 × 8–12

## PROGRAM NO. 40

Program No. 40 is another variation of the Simplified System of Barbell Training, and can be used as a general strength and muscle-building schedule or as a cardio workout. See the instructions for Programs 37, 38 and 39. Note that you'll begin with a set of Trap Bar deadlifts, so you go heavy right at the beginning, which is a bit different than the pattern of weight increases in the standard version of the Simplified System.

This program requires a minimum of a barbell, a Trap Bar, and one set of dumbbells. However, it works better if you can use two barbells and if you have a set of squat stands.

1. Trap Bar deadlift 1 × 12
2. Reverse curl 1 × 12
3. Alternate dumbbell press 1 × 10–12 per arm
4. One-dumbbell side bend 1 × 12 per side
    (50% weight increase for barbell.)
5. Power snatch 1 × 12
6. Power clean and press 1 × 12
7. Barbell bent-over rowing 1 × 12
8. Trap Bar shrug 1 × 12
    (50% weight increase for barbell.)
9. Clean grip high pull 1 × 12
10. Back squat or front squat 1 × 12

# 21

---

# TEN ULTRA-ABBREVIATED
# PROGRAMS FOR OLDER LIFTERS

If you're looking for one of the keys to success for an older lifter, here it is: ultra-abbreviated programs!

Let me say that again.

If you're looking for something that will really work for an older lifter, then give ultra-abbreviated training a try.

Ultra-abbreviated training programs are extremely low-volume programs with a limited number of training days per week and a limited number of exercises. Many workouts consist of only one, two or three exercises. Typically, you perform a limited number of sets (although older trainees may find that they do best if they do plenty of progressively heavier warm-up sets before hitting their "working weights"). Reps are usually in the low to medium range, although some trainees have gotten excellent results from 20-rep squats or 20-rep deadlifts as part of an abbreviated workout.

Ultra-abbreviated training programs were devised for what Peary Rader called "hard cases" and what Bradley J. Steiner and

Stuart McRobert have called "hard-gainers." A hard-gainer is a trainee who has a great deal of difficulty gaining strength and muscle. He doesn't respond well to the standard training program. There's something about his metabolism and his internal functioning that makes the gains come very slowly.

Hard-gainers find that it's very easy to overdo their training. They can almost over-train just by looking at a barbell—or by thinking about training!

You can put a hard-gainer on a standard program of five to eight exercises, performed for a couple of sets each, and he'll end up so stiff, tired and sore that he won't be able to move for a week.

Hard-gainers tend to be fussy eaters. Many foods just don't agree with them. They often find it difficult to gain muscular bodyweight, but easy to gain belly fat.

Hard-gainers typically burn enormous amounts of nervous energy. They get wound up and have difficulty resting. They don't sleep very well. They're always tired and run-down.

Hard-gainers tend to get hurt more often than most trainees. They're the ones who need to focus on squats and deadlifts to pack on the needed pounds, but when they try to do so, they hurt their knees or lower backs. They tend to pull things when they train. They often find that certain standard exercises cause them severe problems. They get extremely sore from a hard workout, and take a long time to recover. Their recuperative powers and recovery ability are very low.

And yet, perhaps because they're so much in need of physical improvement, hard-gainers are often the most enthusiastic trainees out there.

Well, guess what.

As an older lifter, you're officially a hard-gainer. Maybe you didn't used to be—in fact, maybe you were once an easy gainer—a guy who got bigger and stronger just by looking at the weights—but that's what you are now. A hard-gainer.

But being a hard-gainer doesn't mean you can't train. It doesn't mean you can't get good results from your training. Nor does it mean you can't enjoy your training. It just means you have to train more sensibly, more conservatively and more intelligently than ever trained before.

And that's why I use ultra-abbreviated training.

The majority of my current workouts are ultra-abbreviated training programs. I usually train three times a week, on Tuesday, Thursday and Sunday, and I often perform only a single exercise in any workout. That certainly qualifies as ultra-abbreviated training! However, as an older lifter, I need more warm-up sets than when I was younger, so I perform a relatively high number of sets of any particular exercise. But most of the sets are progressively heavier warm-up sets. I rarely exceed five work sets on any particular exercise. And I keep the reps low, even on my warm-up sets, so my total number of reps, and my total training volume, is never very high.

This type of training doesn't sound very spectacular, and it doesn't get much (or any) attention in the mainstream muscle media—but it's been very effective for me. And in the final analysis, that's what counts. Not how often you train, not how long you train, not how many exercises you do, and not how your program compares to the training schedule followed by a group of 20-something year old weightlifting champions in Bulgaria.

If you're an older lifter and you're getting stronger and more powerful—if you're performing your exercises smoothly and efficiently—if your muscle mass is staying where it should be (or even increasing)—if you feel good—if your joints move smoothly and easily—if you don't have too many aches and pains, dings and dents, bangs and bruises—if you approach each workout feeling fresh, strong and hungry for training—and if you look in the mirror and see a little gray (or a lot of gray—or no hair at all), and you can truthfully say, "Hair, schmair! I feel great and it's time to lift!"—then your training program is just what you need.

That's how ultra-abbreviated training makes ME feel—and it can make YOU feel exactly the same way!

## PROGRAM NO. 41

Here's a very basic abbreviated training program. You train twice a week, and do two barbell exercises in each workout, followed by one set of gut work. You use two different workouts and alternate between them.

On your barbell exercises, start light and perform a total of five to seven progressively heavier sets, finishing with one set with your top weight for the day.

Note that on this and all of the other ultra-abbreviated training programs in this chapter, it would be an excellent idea to use a simplified cycling system.

**Mon**

1. General warm-up 10–15 mins
2. Back squat 5–7 progressively heavier sets of 2–5 reps
3. Bench press, incline press, military press or push press 5–7 progressively heavier sets of 2–5 reps
4. Bent-legged sit-up 1 × 8–12

**Thurs**

1. General warm-up 10–15 mins
2. Bent-legged deadlift or Trap Bar deadlift 5–7 progressively heavier sets of 2–5 reps
3. Barbell bent-over rowing 5 progressively heavier sets of 5 reps
4. Hanging knees to chest 1 × 10–15

## PROGRAM NO. 42

Program No. 42 is another two-day per week ultra-abbreviated program. This one is designed for those of you who enjoy using athletic strength training exercises.

See the comments to Program No. 41 for advice on sets, reps, and using a simplified cycling system with this Program.

**Tues**

1. General warm-up 10–15 mins
2. Power Snatch 5 × 2–3
3. Back or front squat 5 × 2–3
4. Bent-legged sit-up 1 × 8–12

**Fri**

1. General warm-up 10–15 mins
2. Power clean 5 × 2
3. Push press or jerk 5 × 2
4. Hanging knees to chest 1 × 10–15

# PROGRAM NO. 43

Here's a three-day per week abbreviated training schedule. This one is designed for those of you who enjoy training with squats, deadlifts (or Trap Bar deadlifts) and military presses, push presses, bench presses or incline presses.

I've used this exact program with excellent results (performing front squats, military presses or push presses, and Trap Bar deadlifts), and I highly recommend it to you.

Follow the instructions on sets, reps and cycling for Program No. 41. Note that when I use this program I begin my front squats and presses with an empty bar and work up until I reach my working weight. On Trap Bar deadlifts I start with 135 pounds and go up from there. For this reason, I do quite a few warm-up sets. If you start heavier (e.g., with 132 or 135 pounds on the bar), you may wish to perform fewer warm-up sets.

For best results, use a 70%–80%–85% and 90–95% cycling program or a similar cycling program.

**Mon**

1. General warm-up 10–15 mins
2. Back squats or front squats 5–7 progressively heavier sets of 2 reps, then 5 × 2 with your top weight for the day.
3. Bent-legged sit-up 1 × 8–12

**Wed**

1. General warm-up 10–15 mins
2. Military press, push press, bench press or incline press 5–7 progressively heavier sets of 2–5 reps, finishing with your top weight for the day for one set.
3. Hanging knees to chest 1 × 10–15.

**Fri**

1. General warm-up 10–15 mins
2. Bent-legged deadlift or Trap Bar deadlift 5–7 progressively heavier sets of 2–5 reps, finishing with your top weight for the day for one set.
3. Plank (1 set), and side plank (1 set to each side)

## PROGRAM NO. 44

Program No. 44 is based on my current program. I use either three or four different exercises and train each movement once a week. This is an excellent program for readers who enjoy athletic strength training exercises.

The comments about sets, reps, warm-ups and cycling in Programs 41, 42 and 43 apply to this program as well.

**Tues**

1. General warm-up 10–15 mins
2. Power snatch 5–7 progressively heavier sets, starting very light and working up to my top weight for the day. I do singles, doubles, triples or sets of five, depending on how I'm feeling, how much training time I have and where I am in my training cycle. Sometimes I do three to five sets with my top weight.
3. Bent-legged sit-up 1 × 8–12

**Thurs**

1. General warm-up 10–15 mins
2. Power clean and press, push press or jerk 5–7 progressively heavier sets, starting light and working up to my top weight for the day. I usually do singles, doubles or triples. On occasion I do either two or three cleans followed by one overhead lift.
3. Hanging leg raise 1 × 10–15

*Note:* Sometimes I do power cleans, and then do presses, push presses or jerks as a separate exercise. The sets and reps are the same for both movements.

**Sun**

1. General warm-up 10–15 mins
2. Back squat or front squat 3–7 progressively heavier sets of 2 reps, then 5 × 2 with your top weight for the day. I always do front squats now, but back squats are fine if you prefer them.
3. Plank (1 set), and side plank (1 set for each side)

# PROGRAM NO. 45

Program No. 45 is an ultra-abbreviated program with five workouts over a two-week period. You train three times in week one and twice in week two. You do two exercises in each workout. You hit your three primary exercises (back squats or front squats, bent-legged deadlifts or Trap Bar deadlifts, and a pressing movement) once a week. You hit each of your auxiliary movements once every two weeks.

The sets and reps are different each week. You'll do three working sets of five reps in week one, and five sets of two with your working weight in week two.

## WEEK ONE

### Mon

1. General warm-up 10–15 mins
2. Back squat or front squat 3–5 progressively heavier warm-up sets, followed by three sets of five reps with your working weight.
3. EZ Bar curl 3–4 × 5–6
4. Bent-legged sit-up 1 × 8–12

### Wed

1. General warm-up 10–15 mins
2. Bench press or incline press 3–5 progressively heavier warm-up sets, followed by three sets of five reps with your working weight.
3. Bent-over barbell row or pull-down to chest 3–5 progressively heavier warm-up sets, followed by three sets of five reps with your working weight.
4. Dumbbell side bend 1 × 10–15 per side

**Fri**

1. General warm-up 10–15 mins
2. Bent-legged deadlift or Trap Bar deadlift 3–5 progressively heavier warm-up sets, followed by three sets of five reps with your working weight.
3. Military press 3–5 progressively heavier warm-up sets, followed by three sets of five reps with your working weight.
4. Hanging knees to chest 1 × 10–15

### Week Two

**Tues**

1. General warm-up 10–15 mins
2. Back squat or front squat 3–5 progressively heavier warm-up sets, followed by five sets of two reps with your working weight.
3. Bench press or incline press 3–5 progressively heavier warm-up sets, followed by five sets of two reps with your working weight.
4. Bent-legged sit-up 1 × 8–12

**Fri**

1. General warm-up 10–15 mins
2. Bent-legged deadlift or Trap Bar deadlift 3–5 progressively heavier warm-up sets, followed by five sets of two reps with your working weight.
3. Hanging knees to chest 1 × 10–15

# PROGRAM NO. 46

Program No. 46 is another program with five workouts spread over a two-week period. You'll train three times in the first week, and two times in the second week.

You'll use squats or front squats, Trap Bar deadlifts and athletic strength training exercises in this program. It's a good program for strength, power, and all-around fitness and conditioning.

This is a low-volume routine, and will work well for older lifters who want to do athletic strength training exercises, but need to limit the amount of work they do.

### WEEK ONE

**Mon**

1. General warm-up 10–15 mins
2. Front squat 5 progressively heavier sets of 2–3 reps, working up to your top weight for the day.
3. Power snatch 5 progressively heavier sets of 2–3 reps, working up to your top weight for the day.
4. Hanging knees to chest 1 × 10–15

**Wed**

1. General warm-up 10–15 mins
2. Power clean 5 progressively heavier sets of 2–3 reps, working up to your top weight for the day.
3. Push press or incline press 3–5 progressively heavier sets of 2–3 reps, working up to your top weight for the day.
4. Plank (1 set), and side plank (1 set per side)

**Fri**

1. General warm-up 10–15 mins
2. Trap Bar deadlifts 5 progressively heavier sets of 2–3 reps, working up to your top weight for the day.
3. Hanging knees to chest 1 × 10–15

## WEEK TWO

**Tues**

1. General warm-up 10–15 mins
2. Back squat 5 progressively heavier sets of 2–3 reps, working up to your top weight for the day.
3. Snatch grip high pull 5 progressively heavier sets of 2–3 reps, working up to your top weight for the day.
4. Bent-legged sit-up 1 × 8–12

**Fri**

1. General warm-up 10–15 mins
2. Clean grip high pull 5 progressively heavier sets of 2–3 reps, working up to your top weight for the day.
3. Jerk 5 progressively heavier sets of 2–3 reps, working up to your top weight for the day.
4. Hanging knees to chest 1 × 10–15

# PROGRAM NO. 47

Program No. 47 is about as ultra-abbreviated as you can get. You train once every four to five days, alternating between two different workouts: Workout A and Workout B. Workout A is a one-exercise workout (plus one set of gut work). In Workout B, you perform two exercises (plus one set of gut work).

This program looks far too simple to work—but for some readers, it will be the very best and most effective program they've ever tried.

## *Workout A*

1. General warm-up 10–15 mins
2. Back squat or front squat 3–5 progressively heavier sets, followed by 1–5 sets with your working weight. Do singles, doubles, or triples.
3. Bent-legged sit-up 1 × 8–12

## *Workout B (performed 4–5 days after Workout A)*

1. General warm-up 10–15 mins
2. Bent-legged deadlift or Trap Bar deadlift 3–5 progressively heavier sets, followed by 1–5 sets with your working weight. Do singles, doubles, or triples.
3. Military press, incline press or bench press 3–5 progressively heavier sets, followed by 1–5 sets with your working weight. Do singles, doubles, or triples.
4. Plank (1 set), and side plank (1 set per side)

## PROGRAM NO. 48

Here's another program where you train once every four to five days. In each workout, you perform two sets of four different exercises. The first set is light. Add weight for the second set. That gives you a total of eight sets, four light and four heavy, in each workout. Simple, but very effective.

This is a very good program for older lifters who have trouble recovering from their workouts. It will be particularly valuable for lifters over the age of sixty. My dad trains on a similar program, and he's in his early eighties.

### *Workout A*

1. General warm-up 10–15 mins
2. EZ Bar curl 2 × 6–8
3. Military press or alternate dumbbell press 2 × 6–8
4. Trap Bar deadlift 2 × 6–8
5. Incline dumbbell press 2 × 6–8

### *Workout B (performed 4–5 days after Workout A)*

1. General warm-up 10–15 mins
2. Back squat or front squat 2 × 6–8
3. Bench press 2 × 6–8
4. Barbell bent-over row, one arm dumbbell row or pull-down to chest 2 × 6–8
5. Bent-legged sit-up 1 × 8–12

# PROGRAM NO. 49

Here's another low-volume program for older lifters. In this schedule, you train three times a week, using a different workout each time you train. You use three to four exercises in each workout and perform your choice of two sets or three sets of each exercise. The first set is light. Add weight for the second set, and add more weight on the third set if you do three sets.

In essence, you're taking a total body workout and dividing it into three different sessions.

**Mon**

1. General warm-up 10–15 mins
2. EZ Bar curl or alternate dumbbell curl 2–3 × 5–6
3. Military press or alternate dumbbell press 2–3 × 5–6
4. Alternate front raise with dumbbells 2–3 × 8–10 per arm
5. Lateral raise 2–3 × 8–10

**Wed**

1. General warm-up 10–15 mins
2. Back squat or front squat 2–3 × 6–8
3. Barbell bench press, incline press, dumbbell bench press or incline dumbbell press 2–3 × 6–8
4. One-arm dumbbell rowing 2–3 × 6–8 per arm

**Fri**

1. General warm-up 10–15 mins
2. Bent-legged deadlift or Trap Bar deadlift 2–3 × 6–8
3. Barbell shrugs, two dumbbell shrugs or Trap Bar shrugs 2–3 × 6–8
4. Bent-legged sit-up 1–2 × 8–12

## PROGRAM NO. 50

Here's a very simple, very effective ultra-abbreviated training program to be performed once every four to seven days. If you're having trouble bouncing back from your training sessions, give this program a try.

On each exercise, do three sets. Use the light/medium/heavy system. Use a light weight on the first set, and add weight for the second set. Add more weight for the third set.

1. General warm-up 10–15 mins
2. Back squat, front squat, or Trap Bar deadlift 3 × 5–6
3. Bench press, incline press, military press or alternate dumbbell press 3 × 5–6
4. Barbell bent-over row, one-arm dumbbell row, or pull-down to chest 3 × 5–6
5. Bent-legged sit-up 1 × 8–12

# 22

## GUT CHECK TIME

As an older lifter, it's very important to keep your gut down. Nothing says "OVER THE HILL" like a great big belly hanging over your belt buckle and making it look as if you had swallowed a watermelon. And it's not just how you look. There's no way to be in good condition with a big gut—and no way to be in good health. A big, bulging belly is linked to diabetes, cardiovascular disease and heart attacks.

In addition, a big gut is going to pull your center of gravity forward—meaning that your spine is going to curve forward—and that's going to lead to lower back problems and a huge loss in lifting ability. Remember, you lift big weights with a flat back. If your spine starts to curve forward, you're going to have trouble doing any kind of heavy lifting.

Now, don't get me wrong. I'm not suggesting that you go on some sort of starvation diet and try to train down to the point where you look like a skinned rabbit. Nor I am suggesting that you strive for the kind of teeny-tiny wasp-waist that makes you look like a teenage boy or an underwear model. If you train for strength and power (as you should, at any age), and if you've been doing it for a long time, your waist is going to be fairly thick—but it will be thick with muscle, not thick with fat. You'll have thick, strong abdominals, thick, strong obliques and thick, strong spinal erectors, all built from long years of heavy lifting.

So what I'm saying is this: no matter what your age, your waist should be reasonably lean and hard—and you should strive to be reasonably lean and hard from head to toe.

If you're not, you need to modify your diet.

There are plenty of diets out there, and plenty of advice on diet and nutrition—much of it conflicting. This is a book about training for older lifters, not a diet and nutrition book, so I'm not going to debate the pros and cons of various diets. But I will share what's worked best for me as I've grown older. It's based on a simple diet featured repeatedly in *Strength & Health*. It's designed for a man who works for a living, trains with heavy weights, and wants to get harder and leaner without losing strength and muscle. The idea is to feed the muscle and starve the fat—and to have enough energy for your daily activities and your training. I've used this one myself with excellent results, and I really like it. (Of course, as with any diet, you should check with your personal physician before giving it a try.)

You eat three big meals a day plus a snack in the afternoon. Breakfast should include plenty of protein, and some high quality carbs. Whole grain bread or toast, whole grains like brown rice or quinoa, hot whole grain cereal, or fresh fruit. Don't go crazy, but fill up and fuel up for the day. You also can try fresh vegetable juice—but stay away from the fresh fruit juice.

For lunch, have a huge green salad with olive oil and vinegar dressing or a big serving of steamed or grilled vegetables, and any sort of lean meat, chicken, turkey or fish—grilled, baked or broiled. No bread, no grain products and no potatoes.

If you get hungry in the afternoon, have a small snack similar to your lunch. Or try some yogurt, cottage cheese or cheese slices and a piece of fresh fruit.

For dinner, have another huge green salad with olive oil and vinegar dressing and another serving of lean meat, chicken, turkey or fish—grilled, baked or broiled. No potatoes. No bread. No grain products.

Drink water, tea, herb tea, fresh vegetable juice and black coffee. No fruit juice, no soft drinks, and nothing with sugar or high fructose corn syrup. No beer, wine or alcohol. No diet colas or diet soft drinks. No milk.

To make the diet work, you need to really get into those big, green salads at lunch and dinner. I'm NOT talking about a little dish of iceberg lettuce. I'm talking about a HUGE salad with a variety of different greens and some fresh chopped or shredded vegetables. Chop, shred, slice and dice everything you can think of, and throw it into the salad.

To give you an idea how it works, here's my menu for today:

## Breakfast

A three-egg omelet with cheddar cheese and half a cup of chopped
fresh herbs and greens: parsley, basil, dill, sage, spinach, salad
greens, cilantro, and chervil.
Two slices of whole grain toast with butter.
Half a cantaloupe or a whole grapefruit
Black coffee

## Lunch

A huge green salad with broad leaf lettuce, Bibb lettuce, spinach,
mixed greens, mache, raw broccoli, chopped celery, shredded

carrot, Swiss chard, red pepper, kale, parsley, cilantro, chervil, sage, basil and dill—with olive oil and vinegar dressing.

8–10 oz. serving of chopped bison—cooked like a hamburger patty—grilled.

## 4:00 snack

Cheese slices and a small green salad or an apple or pear.

## Dinner

Another huge green salad with broad leaf lettuce, Bibb lettuce, spinach, mixed greens, mache, raw broccoli, shredded carrot, Swiss chard, red pepper, kale, parsley, cilantro, chervil, sage, basil and dill—with olive oil and vinegar dressing.

8–10 oz. serving of chopped bison—cooked like a hamburger patty—grilled.

## Supplements

Multi-vitamin/mineral tablet or capsule

Fish oil capsules

Spread your supplements over the different meals. Don't take them all at once.

*Note:* We happen to have several pounds of ground bison in the house, so that's what I'll be having today and tomorrow. It's locally raised, 100% organic, grass-fed bison, which is about as healthy as it gets. You can mix things up as you like. Baked or grilled salmon two or three times a week is a great addition to this diet.

On this diet, I stay lean, hard and muscular at a bodyweight of 220–225 pounds (at 5′9″). I have plenty of energy for training and for my daily activities, and I don't feel hungry or deprived. It's an easy diet to follow and doesn't require lots of time in the kitchen.

The diet comes with another big plus for older lifters. It's very high in foods that are ranked high in anti-inflammatory factors, such as fresh vegetables and herbs, free-range eggs, grass-fed bison and grass-fed beef, salmon, fish oil and olive oil. In fact, if you run the numbers, the daily diet ends up with an off-the chart anti-inflammatory rating. And since our workouts are a constant source of inflammation, a diet that is high in anti-inflammatory factors is probably a very good thing for an older lifter. I know it makes an important difference in my own training.

But remember—this is the diet that works best for me. It may not work for you. Consult your personal physician before giving this or any other diet a try!

# 23

---

# CORE TRAINING FOR
# OLDER LIFTERS

In the previous chapter I discussed the importance of staying lean, hard and muscular, and covered a very effective diet and nutritional program for older lifters—one that was featured in *Strength & Health* magazine many years ago, and one that has worked very well for me over the past few years.

Now it's time to talk about a related issue—core training for older lifters.

Based on some of my comments in the previous chapter, you might think that I'm going to suggest an all-out program of high-rep abdominal exercises to whip that midsection into shape.

Actually, that's the LAST thing I would suggest for an older lifter.

I tried a high-rep ab program for an entire summer two years ago (at age 49 going on 50). I was curious. I wanted to see what would happen. I had always performed low sets of low to medium reps with weight resistance for my gut work, and it had worked well. But after a shoulder injury limited many of my training options (for example, no more hanging leg raises), I decided to experiment with high reps for a while.

In short order I was doing every type of crunch you can imagine, as well as a variety of other core movements. I worked up to several hundred reps, and eventually moved up to 1,000 reps per workout. Some with weight and some without. Some fast, and some very slow with constant tension on the muscles.

Two things happened. I was dieting pretty hard, and as a result, I got very lean and muscular. It looked like I had abs on my abs. Not bad for a 50-year old guy who weighed 220 pounds.

But something else happened. My lower back got stiff and sore like you wouldn't believe. And it started to lock up on me. I'd be sitting down, and when I stood up, my lower back would go into a painful spasm. Sometimes I had trouble standing or walking normally.

The ART specialist who was working on my shoulder also worked on the low back spasms. He thought they were caused by very strong and very tight psoas muscles—the result of many years of heavy ab training on movements such as sit-ups and leg raises, which work the psoas muscles very heavily. He also thought the high-rep crunches were contributing to the problem.

I dropped the reps and my lower back felt better—and then I did something extreme. I dropped the crunches completely and started to do front squats again after not having done them for several years.

Have you ever seen a photo of a modern day Olympic weightlifter in one of the light or medium weight classes? Some of them look like their abs are jumping right through their skin. They have amazing abdominal development. And they don't get it from crunches—or from any sort of gut work. They get it from lifting and supporting enormous weights in the overhead positions of the snatch and jerk—and from doing plenty of squat cleans and front squats.

Think about it. When you perform a back squat, your lower back muscles stabilize your spine and keep the weight of the bar from driving you down and forward. When you perform a front squat, your abs do the stabilization work. Thus, the front squat gives your abs a tremendous isometric workout. It's almost exactly the same as performing a plank.

In any event, I stopped doing crunches and started to do front squats again, after not having done them for several years. And the results have been pretty good. I no longer suffer from those crippling low back spasms, and my abs are hard and muscular and strong—and it's all the result of doing front squats on a regular basis, along with the other staples in my training program: power snatches, power cleans, push presses and jerks.

I should mention that I don't wear a belt, so my abs provide all the support on my front squats. That probably makes them a much more effective ab exercise for me. Also, I have short legs and a long torso—and that means my abs have to work extra hard to stabilize my spine when I perform front squats. Lifters who wear a belt or who have a different body type might find they need to include direct ab movements.

Also, don't forget that I have a long history of heavy ab work. Lifters who have never done much ab work are in a different situation.

Training your abs with front squats is probably not the best way for everyone to train their abs, but it works well for me at this stage of my career. And who knows? I may add some direct ab exercises into my program sometime in the future. But right now, the front squats are doing the trick.

I'm an extreme case, but I believe that the majority of older lifters need to limit their ab training to avoid lower back problems.

285

A few sets in each workout will work fine. As far as exercises go, try bent-legged sit-ups, leg raises, side bends, hanging knees to chest, planks and side planks or crunches. (Don't do them all in one workout—use one movement each time you train, and alternate between two or three different core exercises.) Use low to medium reps. If you train with added weight, don't go super-heavy. Save it for other exercises.

Planks are a good choice for older lifters. They help to stabilize your entire midsection, and tie your upper and lower body together. And they're much easier on your lower back than most ab exercises. Just be sure you keep your back flat when you do them, and don't "sag" at the hips.

The bottom line is this. You need to work your abs. If you can work your midsection with front squats, like I do, that's great. If you need to do more direct ab work, then do it. Keep those midsection muscles strong and powerful.

# 24

## PROTECTING YOUR JOINTS

As an older lifter, one of the most important things to do is to protect your joints. (And no, I'm not talking about hanging onto your stash.) I'm talking about protecting your knees and ankles—your hips and lower back—your shoulders, elbows, and wrists. And while we're at it, let's talk about protecting your hands and feet as well. If you don't protect them, your joints are going to give you problems—and quite likely end your lifting career.

Now, I'm not a medical doctor, and I'm not going to give you any medical advice. If you have a specific question about a joint problem, find a qualified medical professional and get it checked out. Don't ask your training partners, don't ask the guys at the gym, and don't get on a discussion board and start asking total strangers about what to do. Joint problems are far too important to leave to non-experts.

I'm a lifter—a 52-year old lifter—and I'm going to share some commonsense tips about how to manage your training to help minimize (and hopefully avoid) joint problems. I'll tell you about some things that I do to avoid joint problems, and some things that have helped me work through various bumps, bruises, dings and dents over the years. Hopefully, you'll never have to deal with a serious joint problem—but if you ever do, get it checked out FAST by a medical professional.

## EXERCISE SELECTION

One of the most important ways for an older lifter to avoid serious injury is to train safely and conservatively, and that begins with safe and conservative exercise selection. I covered this in detail, and I'm not going to repeat myself, but I do want to remind you to be very careful in your choice of exercises. There are many movements that are simply not a good idea for an older lifter.

Also, be very cautious when adding a new exercise to your training program. Start very light, learn the movement, and add weight slowly. Give your body plenty of time to adapt to the new movement. This is really important for older lifters.

And whatever you do, don't make the mistake of failing to treat an exercise as a "new" movement just because it's something you used to do five, ten or twenty years ago. If you're not doing it on a regular, consistent basis, it's a new exercise even if there was a time when you used to do it every time you trained.

I'll give you a case in point. It involves Tommy Kono, who may very well have been the greatest Olympic weightlifter of all time.

In 1959, after he had already won two Olympic Gold medals and five world championships in Olympic weightlifting, Tommy was doing an exhibition in Dover, Pennsylvania. At the time, his best snatch in competition was 297 pounds. Tommy performed his competition snatches in the squat style, and trained on the squat-style of lifting. However, in the exhibition, he wanted to demonstrate the split-style of lifting as well as the squat-style, so he performed a split snatch with 135 pounds—less than half of his best competition lift, and a very light weight for the world and Olympic champion.

Tommy tweaked his right knee on that lift.

At the 1959 world championships in Warsaw, Poland, Tommy attempted a world record of 374 pounds in the clean and jerk. He cleaned the weight but missed the jerk. The next day, after spending several hours on his feet, he tried to sit down. His right knee was so stiff, sore and swollen that he could not bend it enough to sit. His right knee bothered him for the rest of his career—and it led him to shift more effort to his left leg in training and in competition—which led to a sore left knee. By the time of the 1960 Olympic Games in Rome, Tommy's knees were so sore he could not perform full deep knee bends or stress his legs in any other way without causing severe pain.

If something like that can happen to a lifter the caliber of Tommy Kono, it can certainly happen to anyone else! So whatever you do, be very careful about using new exercises—or about trying something you used to do a long time ago, but haven't done for awhile.

## "DANCE WITH WHO BRUNG YA!"

That's a good way to avoid getting shot in a Texas honky-tonk, and it's a good way for an older lifter to stay healthy. If you built up by following a powerlifting program as a young lifter, you're probably going to do best by sticking to powerlifting when you get older. If you become interested in Olympic weightlifting and try to start it at a relatively late point in your training career, you may be setting yourself up for an injury, particularly if you don't have a qualified lifting coach or if you try to rush things and train too heavy too soon.

The same is true of an older lifter who decides to switch from bodybuilding to powerlifting—from bodybuilding to Olympic weightlifting—from bodybuilding, powerlifting or weightlifting to strongman training—from powerlifting or weightlifting to bodybuilding—from lifting "raw" to lifting with a belt, wraps and suit—from lifting with a belt to lifting without a belt and vice-versa—to handling a regular barbell to handling a thick-handled barbell—from parallel squats to full squats—from full range reps to heavy partials in the power rack and vice-versa—from any type of lifting to high rep bodyweight training—from body-weight training to any type of lifting—from barbell and dumb-bell training to kettlebell work—from kettlebells to barbells and dumbbells—from cardio training to any type of lifting—from any type of lifting to cardio training—from lifting to any sport—and from any sport to lifting.

I'm not saying you can never change how you train. But if you do, you need to take things slow and easy. You need to be patient and conservative. It took a long time to develop a particular way of doing things—and if you change what you're doing, you need to be very cautious.

Remember Dizzy Dean, the baseball pitcher who burst into the major leagues with a blazing fastball. He was an absolute phenom. But one day, a line drive hit the dirt in front of him and bounced up and hit his toe. This caused him to change his pitching motion—and as a result, he blew out his arm. That sore toe ended up ruining his career as a major league pitcher.

Or go back to the example of Tommy Kono hurting his right knee when doing split-style snatches in an exhibition. Look at what happened. His right knee started to give him big trouble, and he compensated by shifting more effort to his left leg—and then he developed problems with his left knee.

## SETS AND REPS

This is another point we've covered before, but it bears repeating in the context of joint protection. Here's the bottom line: you only have a limited number of reps of any particular exercise in your body. Use them wisely. Don't wear out your joints with unnecessary reps or meaningless movements. Make everything you do count.

Older lifters will almost always do better with low reps. This is particularly true when it comes to squats and deadlifts. Many older lifters find that anything over five reps in the squat will quickly lead to knee inflammation—that triples are better than sets of five—that doubles are great—and that singles also work very well. Not maximum effort, gut-busting, slow-motion, torture reps—but reps that are crisp and smooth and under perfect control all the way up and all the way down.

Let me repeat that. For many older lifters, anything over five reps in the squat is going to cause knee inflammation. Threes are usually better than fives. Doubles and singles work very well. Not with super heavy weights, but with weights that you can control all the way up and all the way down.

Sure, you could train harder. You could do more sets and more reps. And it might even work for a few workouts. But if you overdo things, sooner or later you're going to wake up with a nagging pain in your knees—and that may mean you have to stop squatting for a long, long time. So in the end, pushing too hard and grinding out rep after rep is counter-productive for an older lifter.

As an older lifter, you have several training goals. One is to get stronger and better conditioned. Another is to stay healthy. A third goal is to be able to lift for the rest of your life. If you push too hard for strength gains, you'll hurt yourself—and that may make healthy lifting and life-long training impossible.

Play it safe. Limit your sets and reps. Do NOT overtrain.

## WEIGHT ON THE BAR

Here's another point that requires some mental re-conditioning. We all grew up learning to pile as much weight on the bar as possible. Heavier was always better. The more weight on the bar, the better the workout. We weren't happy unless the bar bent like a pretzel, the platform shuddered, the squat stands looked like they were going to buckle and a nearby scientist registered our workout as an 8.7 on the Richter Scale.

For a younger lifter, that's how you have to think in order to progress. But for an older lifter, it's almost always going to lead to injury.

That's a very important point, so pay careful attention. Too many older lifters keep trying to pile more and more weight on the bar, without stopping to consider how much weight their body can handle—and without stopping to consider whether it's really necessary for them to train "that heavy." In most cases, it isn't. Remember the example of Master's weightlifting champions who typically train in the 70% to 80–85% range. They've found what works for an older lifter. Follow their example.

# CYCLING

As an older lifter, you need to train in cycles. Start light, work up, repeat. Four-week cycles are excellent, in part because you can change exercises around after each cycle. Sticking to the same exercises all the time may aggravate wear and tear on your joints.

Do NOT make the mistake of trying to train at 100% all the time. As an older lifter, you just can't do it—nor should you try.

# AVOID OVERTRAINING

Avoid overtraining like the plague. Overtraining is the bugaboo of almost every older lifter—and overtraining is one of the primary causes of joint problems for older lifters.

There are many ways to overtrain. You can overtrain by training too often. You can overtrain by training too long. You can overtrain by doing too many exercises, too many sets, and too many reps. You can overtrain by training too heavy, and you can overtrain by working at too high a level of intensity.

Older lifters will do best on abbreviated training programs— and many will do best on ultra-abbreviated schedules. My own training typically consists of one exercise per workout, and three workouts per week. That's an example of ultra-abbreviated program. Doesn't sound like much, but it's very effective. And it's effective because it helps me avoid overtraining.

If you follow any of the programs in this book (or any other program, including a program of your own design) and you don't gain as well as you want—or if you start to feel tired and sore all the time —or if your joints begin to bother you, then DO LESS. Train lighter, train less frequently, and do fewer exercises. Doing less is almost always better than doing more.

## WARM-UPS

Warm-ups are critical for older lifters. You need a 10–15 minute general warm-up before you begin strength training—and after that you need to start very light and gradually add weight to the bar over a series of progressive sets before you get up to your working weight on any particular exercise. Warm-ups get the blood moving through your body, loosen your joints, and—very importantly—get your heart, lungs and circulatory system ready for hard training. Younger lifters often ignore their warm-ups—but older lifters should always pay very careful attention to their warm-ups.

And please remember—you should start light AND slow. There's nothing to be gained by using a light weight and banging the reps out as fast as possible. Your first set might be with a very light weight (perhaps an empty bar) and you might perform it at about 50% of your top speed. As you gradually add weight to the bar, gradually increase your speed of movement. Make your warm-ups progressive both in weight AND in speed of movement.

Your warm-up is one of the most important parts of your workout. Do it right. Get your mind into it. Focus. Concentrate. Make every movement count. Feel the way your body responds as you go through your standard drill. Your warm-up is the time when your body will tell you if there's a problem—for example, if you're not fully recovered from a previous training session or if you're suffering from a dent or ding that hasn't healed. Pay careful attention and listen to those signals.

Your body may tell you that even though today is scheduled to be a heavy day, going heavy is just not a good idea. If that's what your body tells you, then LISTEN—and take a light workout—and come back and do the heavy stuff another day. (This one rule alone may save you from a devastating injury.)

# ICE

Ice is an older lifter's friend. It helps immeasurably in controlling joint inflammation after a hard workout. Baseball pitchers ice their arms after every game. Lifters should do the same after every training session. It really helps.

Icing your knees and shoulders after you train them is particularly good for controlling soreness and inflammation.

## HOT TUBS AND WHIRLPOOLS

I don't have any personal experience with hot tubs or whirlpools, but many older lifters swear by them. If you have access to them, they make a great addition to your training. Many Master's weightlifters and Master's powerlifters are big fans of hot tubs and whirlpools. At the very least, make sure you follow your workouts with a good, hot shower, and let the water really work on those sore spots.

## CHIROPRACTIC AND MASSAGE

If you have the time and money, and access to a good chiropractor, ART therapist or anyone who knows how to perform sports massage, then make the most of it. A good chiropractor or massage professional can add years to your lifting.

## FISH OIL

There are plenty of over-hyped (and largely useless) supplements out there, but there's also one product that's pretty good: fish oil. Fish oil is an omega 3 powerhouse. Omega 3's are excellent for joint health, and help fight soreness, stiffness and inflammation. And this is not just supplement company marketing hype. This is from peer-reviewed medical journals and legitimate research studies from around the world.

I started using fish oil for the first time back in 2006. Several months earlier I had (very foolishly) gone out and done some hill sprints for cardio work. After two or three sessions of hill sprints, my Achilles tendons were so sore and inflamed I wondered if I was ever going to be able to walk again. They stayed sore for several months—and didn't start feeling better until I began taking the fish oil.

Six months later, we ran out of fish oil and I stopped taking it—and gradually, over time, the soreness and stiffness started to come back. I began taking the fish oil again, and my ankles felt much better. That sold me on the merits of fish oil, and I've been taking it ever since.

## LIFTING BELTS

Many people think that lifting belts are essential for protecting against low back injuries. Actually, they're not. They can help, but for anyone other than a competitive powerlifter, they're not an essential piece of safety equipment.

Lifting belts help protect the low back by giving your abdominal muscles something to push against when you perform a heavy lift. By pushing against the belt, your abdominals form a powerful corset of muscle that helps hold the spine in proper alignment as you perform the lift.

From that description, it becomes obvious that a lifting belt doesn't work unless you pull it really tight. Just wearing the belt doesn't do anything. It's the combination of the tight belt and the contraction of your abdominal muscles that does the trick.

You can achieve the same thing by strengthening your abdominal muscles. If your midsection is strong and powerful, you really don't need to use a belt for anything—unless you are a competitive powerlifter, in which case, feel free to use the belt for truly heavy squats and deadlifts.

Olympic weightlifters often compete without belts. This is because a weightlifter needs to pull the bar very close to his body when performing the snatch and clean, and the belt buckle gets in the way. Some lifters have actually missed lifts when the bar hit their belt buckle!

I stopped using a belt when I was in my late 30's or early 40's because I was no longer competing in powerlifting competition, and because I was doing more power cleans and power snatches in my workouts. At first, it was difficult to lift heavy weights without using the belt. I felt weak and unstable. But over time I learned how to lift without the belt, and I've never gone back to using one. I believe lifting without a belt has made me stronger, especially in the mid-section.

The bottom line is this. If you prefer to use a lifting belt, that's fine—but use it the right way. Pull it tight and snug and make it mean something. And if you prefer to train without a belt, that's fine, too. There's no rule that says you HAVE to wear one!

If you have been using a belt, and you decide to train without one, be very careful at first. Things are going to feel "different" for a while. Give your body time to get used to lifting without a belt.

## KNEE WRAPS

Knee wraps are like lifting belts. Some people think they're an essential piece of safety equipment. Others think they do little or nothing to protect your knees—and others believe they actually lead to knee injuries. A top powerlifting coach and meet director once told me that any time a lifter hurt his knee either at a meet or in training, he asked him if he trained with knee wraps—and the answer from the injured lifter was always the same: "Yes, I wear them all the time." This coach believed that if you wore wraps all the time, you failed to strengthen your knee tendons, and sooner or later they'd give out on you under a heavy squat.

In a similar vein, Peary Rader always believed that wrapping your knees was actually dangerous because it caused the knee joint to pull apart under a heavy load—especially if you did the old "drop and bounce."

When I trained for competitive powerlifting, I wore knee wraps when I squatted. When I stopped powerlifting, I stopped wearing them. I never had any knee injuries when I wore them, and (knock on wood), I've not had any since I stopped wearing them. But I prefer not to wear them.

If you wear knee wraps, you are forced to perform parallel squats. It's virtually impossible to perform a full squat or front squat while wearing heavy-duty, super-tight knee wraps. Ten or twelve years ago, I switched from doing parallel squats to doing full back squats and full front squats—and today I train my legs exclusively with full range, butt to the floor front squats—and that means, no knee wraps.

Be aware that if you've been using knee wraps and you try to train without them, it's going to take some time to readjust. Don't go too heavy at first, and build the weight up gradually. Your knee tendons will require some time to get conditioned to lifting without knee wraps.

## SQUAT SUITS

You can make a good argument that belts and knee wraps are really performance enhancers rather than safety equipment—and the argument goes double for squat suits. They'll certainly help you lift more weight in powerlifting competition, but they don't serve any sort of safety function. Unless you're a competitive powerlifter, there's no need for them.

## BENCH SHIRTS

Unlike the squat suit, the bench shirt really does help a powerlifter protect against shoulder injuries when he's performing a heavy lift. But if you're not a powerlifter, you may not even be doing bench presses, and you certainly don't need to perform heavy singles.

As an older lifter, you need to be aware that the bench shirt pulls your shoulders forward, creating a funny round-shouldered look that mimics age-related deterioration of the thoracic and cervical spine. I have to think that can't be very good for you.

## KNEE SLEEVES

Knee sleeves are a great boon for older lifters. Unlike knee wraps, they don't help you lift more weight, and they don't provide any actual protection for the knee. Instead, they keep your knees warm. As a result, your knees will be better lubricated, more mobile and less stiff when you train—and that's a really good thing!

Knee sleeves were invented by World and Olympic Games champion Tommy Kono, who started to have knee problems when he was in his 30's. Tommy lived in Hawaii at the time, and one day he cut the legs from an old scuba-diving suit and made himself a pair of knee sleeves—and immediately discovered that they made his knees feel much better when he trained. He shared the idea with Bob Hoffman, and before long the York Barbell Company was selling knee sleeves. York doesn't carry them any more, but you can buy them directly from Tommy Kono at www.tommykono.com. You also can order knee sleeves from Bud Charniga at www.dynamic-eleiko.com

## WAISTBANDS

Tommy Kono also sells waistbands, which, like his knee sleeves, are designed to provide warmth and heat rather than to provide support. They're not lifting belts, or a replacement for lifting belts. Rather, they're a way of keeping your waist and lower back warm while you train. I've never used one, so I can't speak for their effectiveness, but it might be something for an older lifter to look into.

## SWEATSUITS

If sweat pants and sweatshirts had not already been invented, they'd need to be invented just for older lifters! They're that important. Sweat clothing helps you retain body heat and stay warm when you train. It makes it easier to warm up, and it keeps you warm throughout your workout. It keeps you from cooling down and getting cold halfway through your workout—and believe me, it's no fun to have a cold and clammy t-shirt sticking to your back.

I train in an unheated garage, and although we don't have New England style winters in Louisville, it does get cold sometimes. So in the wintertime, I take a page from Reg Park's book, and wear double sweats when I train.

In the summer, things get pretty hot, but I still wear sweat pants and a sweatshirt with the neck cut big and the sleeves cut off below the elbows.

As an older lifter, it's very important to stay warm when you train. Sweat clothes are the way to dress for success. The color is optional, but dark gray, navy blue and black work pretty well for most of us.

## LIFTING SHOES

Older lifters need to support their feet. Never train barefoot or in sandals. It works fine for the Muscle Beach crowd, but it's not recommended for older lifters. If you're an older lifter, you need to wear strong shoes with sturdy arch supports. Your feet take plenty of abuse over the years, and after enough of it, they can start to cause problems.

And please note this. Your ankles and Achilles tendons become more and more vulnerable as you grow older. This is because they don't have much of a blood supply. Strong shoes help to protect your ankles as well as your feet.

I switched to Olympic lifting shoes seven or eight years ago, and I really like them. They're required equipment for anyone who does athletic style strength training, but even if you stick to squats, deadlifts, Trap Bar deadlifts, presses and similar movements, they're a good investment.

Some older lifters like to wear hiking boots or construction shoes when they train. I've never tried them, but it makes sense, and it would be a good alternative to lifting shoes.

# EQUIPMENT

As an older lifter, you don't need to take chances with second-rate equipment. If you're going to train, do it right. The last thing you need is an unnecessary injury caused by old, poorly maintained or low-quality equipment.

If you train with adjustable dumbbells, make sure the collars are tight and secure. You don't need a plate sliding off at the wrong time.

If you train at home, do NOT do bench presses outside of a power rack. Do you remember Dick the Bruiser? For many years, the barrel-chested, thickly-muscled Bruiser was one of the toughest, roughest and meanest men in professional wrestling. He died at age 61, after rupturing a blood vessel in his esophagus while training alone in his basement. He was doing bench presses when it happened. I don't know if he got stuck under the bar, or if he almost got stuck and had to fight the bar back into the racks—but whatever happened, it wasn't good. And if it can happen to Dick the Bruiser, it can happen to anyone.

For obvious reasons, always train your squats in a power rack, as well.

If you train in a home gym, keep your training quarters neat and clean. My stepson and his buddies once did an oil change inside the garage where I train. They did it once and once only. Then they got the message. The garage is for training. Period. No one tracks mud or dirt inside, no one spills anything, and no one does anything that might cause a slip and fall.

## IF YOU DO GET INJURED . . .

No matter what you do or how intelligently you train, you may get injured. It's an unavoidable risk of any physical activity—especially if you're over the age of 40.

If you DO get injured, don't try to tough it out. See a doctor—preferably a sports medicine doctor who understands athletic injuries.

Many times, your doctor will tell you to take some time off and REST the injured body-part or the injured joint. Sometimes, that's hard to do—but it's often the only way to keep a relatively minor problem from becoming a chronic, serious problem. Many dings and dents are really over-use injuries—in essence, the result of overtraining—and the only way to get healed up is to take either a complete break from your training or, at the least, to stop doing the movement or movements that seem to be causing the problem.

Note that a break from training does not have to be a break from all physical activity. There's a difference between giving an injured elbow time to heal by avoiding any curling or pulling movements for a few weeks and doing nothing at all. Last year I broke and severely dislocated my left index finger, and sprained two other fingers on that hand pretty badly. I spent two weeks with my hand in a cast, followed by three months of therapy where I was under doctor's orders not to do any lifting. The only exercise I could do was front squats with my arms crossed and my hands on top of the bar (bodybuilder style front squats), so I trained those and nothing else until I was cleared to go back to regular training.

## LIGHT EXERCISE CAN HELP

If your doctor says it's okay, light exercise can be a tremendous help when you're trying to recover from an injury. In February, 2007, when I was 49 years old, I developed a very severe shoulder problem as the result of overly-aggressive yoga training. I woke up one morning with my left shoulder so stiff and sore that I could not lift it above parallel. The problem persisted, and eventually I ended up seeing an orthopedic surgeon, who performed a detailed examination and cheerfully announced that although he wasn't sure what the problem was, exploratory surgery "couldn't hurt."

"Everyone your age has plenty of arthritic spurring," he said. "We'll go in and clean it all out and see what happens."

He suggested that we schedule the surgery as soon as possible.

I decided to get a second opinion—and visited an ART specialist who happens to have an office just a few miles away from the house. He thought I had a frozen shoulder or an impingement syndrome of some sort. He was appalled at the idea of doing surgery for the mere sake of doing surgery, and suggested that we try a program of ART sessions two or three times a week, combined with plenty of very light remedial exercises. (ART is "Active Release Therapy"—a form of deep-tissue, trigger-point massage that works extremely well for many athletic injuries.)

That led to some of the funniest workouts you can imagine. I started out doing ridiculously high reps (50 or more per set) of lateral raises, front raises, bent-over lateral raises, curls, hammer curls, and one-arm rowing with 2 ½ pound plates! I kept the garage doors closed so no one would walk by and laugh at me.

Eventually, I progressed to light dumbbells, and soon I was doing bodybuilder style shoulder workouts where I spent 45 minutes doing every different shoulder raise ever invented, and many that I invented right there in the garage for the sole purpose of hitting the shoulders from all angles and getting as much blood as possible to flow through my shoulders.

Gradually, over the course of five or six months, I got back to the point where I could raise my arm all the way over my head again. That doesn't sound like much, but if my problem was a "frozen shoulder," which seems to be the most accurate diagnosis, I came back two or three times as fast as patients typically do—and I did it without cortisone shots and without surgery. The ART sessions deserve the lion's share of the credit here, but the light reps certainly helped.

## COMING BACK FROM AN INJURY

If you've had to take a lay-off from training as a result of an injury, or if you've had to avoid certain exercises for a while as the result of an injury, be very careful when you resume your regular program. The first few steps on the comeback trail can be very dangerous. This is because everyone always tries to go too heavy too soon—and before you know it, you end up hurting yourself again.

There's a much better way to do things. It takes longer (in the short run), and it's a bit boring, but it's much safer and much more likely to work for you.

I'll explain how to do it, using the example of a lifter who has had a shoulder injury and has not been able to do any overhead lifting for several months. He's stayed in shape with Trap Bar deadlifts, front squats, barbell bent-over rowing, gut work, and some very light lateral raises, front raises and bent-over lateral raises. Now he has the green light to start doing presses again. (Yes, I'm using myself as an example. This is how I came back after my frozen shoulder.)

This is what our lifter should do. On the first day that he's released to train without restriction, he should do overhead presses with nothing but an empty broomstick or a 7′ length of PVC pipe. He should NOT use any weight. He should use ONLY the broomstick or the PVC pipe, and he should move very slowly and carefully. Yeah, I KNOW there's no weight on the bar, and I KNOW this isn't a "workout." That's fine. It's not supposed to be a workout. Our lifter's not training. Rather, he's testing his shoulder to see if he can go through a full range movement without pain.

If all goes well, the lifter can try using an empty barbell in his next workout. However, if he feels ANY pain or discomfort whatsoever, he should stay with the broomstick or PVC pipe and not add any weight. After all, if it hurts when you use a broomstick, it's not going to feel any better if you go heavier.

If the empty bar feels okay, the lifter should add weight in his next workout. Not very much. Five or ten pounds will be plenty. And again, he's not doing any actual "training." Rather, he's trying to determine if he can move through a full range of motion without pain.

Our lifter can perform overhead presses three times a week (or even more often) because he's not training for strength, but rather, is trying to regain mobility. Daily training at this stage of the game is fine.

Our lifter should take it slow and easy, and add five (or at most, ten) pounds to the bar each workout (if training three times a week) or every second or third workout (if training more often). That doesn't sound like much, but if you train three times per week and add five pounds per workout, that's 15 pounds a week—60 pounds a month—120 pounds in two months—and 180 pounds in three months. If you train three times a week and add ten pounds per workout, that's 30 pounds a week—120 pounds in one month—and 240 pounds in two months. That ought to be fast enough progress for anyone.

In any event, our lifter should keep on training very slowly, methodically and carefully, adding weight in small increments, and taking his time to get back to his pre-injury strength levels. As I said, I know it's not much fun, and I know you're going to want to go faster—but when you're coming back from an injury you need to be very careful not to re-injure yourself. Slow and steady is the way to go.

# 25

## THE WRAP-UP

It's a blazing hot summer day in Louisville. There's an old house on a hill with a vegetable garden in the back yard, and a couple of lazy cats lying in the shade on the porch.

In back of the house there's an old garage with the door wide open. Inside the garage there's a thick, muscular man with glasses. He has dark hair streaked with gray. His face is covered with chalk and dripping with sweat.

Despite the heat, he's wearing sweat pants and an old gray sweatshirt with the neck cut out and the sleeves cut off below the elbows.

He's standing on a homemade wooden platform, facing two heavy-duty squat stands. Vulcan Racks from IronMind.

On top of the racks is an Eleiko bar, loaded with an assortment of rubber bumper plates.

The sound track to *Rocky Balboa* is playing in the background.

The gray-haired lifter flexes his hands, steps toward the bar, takes a deep breath and gets into position.

You can tell he's been doing this for many years—and you also can tell that he plans to keep on doing it for many years to come.

The gray-haired lifter racks the bar, steps back, plants his feet, and performs two deep, full reps in the front squat. Each rep is performed under perfect control. There's no doubt. No hesitation. No question.

He drives up out of the hole, stands tall, steps forward, and racks the bar.

One work set down. Four to go. It's going to be another another great workout.

⫷ ⫷ ⫷

We've come a long way together, you and I. We've covered plenty of ground. I've given you my best, most candid insight into serious strength training for older lifters. I've tried to make this book as detailed and complete as possible, and while I've not been able to cover everything under the sun, I've tried to cover the most important points.

I hope you've enjoyed the book, and that you will follow and benefit from the advice in it—and that you will continue to do so for a very long time.

Thanks for reading this book —thanks for continuing to hit the iron hard and heavy—and thanks for setting a great example for everyone else, young and old alike.

From one older lifter to another, I salute you. Good luck—and best wishes for life-long strength and health!

# ABOUT THE AUTHOR

Brooks Kubik is a 52-year old weightlifter who grew up following the York Training System and the teachings of the men who wrote for *Strength and Health*—including Bob Hoffman, Steve Stanko, John Grimek, Bradley J. Steiner and Harry Paschall, supplemented by training advice from Peary Rader and others in *Iron Man* magazine. Weight training allowed Brooks to overcome severe childhood asthma and become an award-winning athlete, the captain of his high school wrestling team, and a state champion in Greco-Roman wrestling. Brooks later competed in powerlifting and bench press contests and won many titles in drug-tested competition, including five national championships in the Submaster's division in bench press competition.

Brooks is the author of *Dinosaur Training: Lost Secrets of Strength and Development,* a book that became an international best seller and that has been called "the bible of strength training." In 2008 and 2009 he published *Legacy of Iron* and *Clouds of War,* which chronicle weightlifting in the 1930's and 40's in a unique novel format that gives unparalleled insights into the Golden Age of Might and Muscle and the legendary champions of the era.

311

Brooks is currently hard at work on the third volume of the Legacy of Iron series, as well as other exciting publications covering no-nonsense strength training and muscle building.

When he's not writing and researching, Brooks trains hard and heavy in his garage gym—and whenever he can, he squeezes in some work in his backyard vegetable garden.

Brooks lives in Louisville, Kentucky with his beautiful wife, Trudi. They are the proud parents of three children (Dan, Paul and Lily) and two grandchildren (Olivia and Sadie).

Be sure to visit Brooks' website at www.brookskubik.com and sign up for his daily email messages and training tips from Dinosaur Headquarters!

# If You Like This Publication, Then You Will Love This Catalog!

The largest stock of strength-related publications available in the world! Titles you never knew existed. Many not advertised anywhere. New and out-of-print books, courses, rare collector's items, etc. Information on functional strength, strongmen, bodybuilding, powerlifting, feats of strength, biographies, muscle control, nutrition, specialization, muscular bulk, definition, etc.

You'll find classic instruction by all the recognized world authorities Otto Arco, Paul Anderson, Edward Aston, Mark Berry, Alan Calvert, Anthony Ditillo, Hermann Goerner, John Grimek, George Hackenschmidt, Thomas Inch, John Jesse, George Jowett, Ed Jubinville, Charles MacMahon, Maxick, Reg Park, Harry Paschall, Bob Peoples, William Pullum, Peary Rader, Michael J. Salvati, Arthur Saxon, David P. Willoughby, etc.

**Harry Paschall** was a prolific writer for Bob Hoffman's *Strength and Health* magazine. In addition, he wrote several books such as: *Muscle Moulding, Development of Strength, Muscular Arms and Shoulders*, and *The Bosco System of Physical Training*. His books are available here!

**George F. Jowett** founded *The Jowett Institute of Health and Physical Culture* back in the 1930's.

He edited *Strength* magazine, helped Bob Hoffman start his *Strength and Health* magazine, manufactured equipment, etc. His famous mail order course and the classic *Key to Might and Muscle* are available here too!

**Alan Calvert** founded *Milo Bar Bell Company* in 1902, published *Strength* magazine and wrote the famous book *Super Strength* as well as *The Milo Bar Bell Courses*. His publications can be found here.

*The Mark Berry Bar Bell Courses* can be found in this amazing catalog as well as *The Text Book of Weight-Lifting* by Arthur Saxon, *The Way to Live* by George Hackenschmidt, *Goerner the Mighty* by Edgar Mueller, *Muscle Control* by Maxick, etc.

Hailed by cellar dwellers, garage gorillas and back yard lifters as the number one single source for the highest quality, result producing physical training information available today! So, don't delay...

**Send for your free illustrated catalog today. You'll like it!**

**Bill Hinbern**
**32430-K Cloverdale St.**
**Farmington, Michigan**
**48336-4008**
**USA**

**www.superstrengthtraining.com**
**info@superstrengthtraining.com**

# Reg Park

**Mr. Universe 1951, 1958, 1965**
**(World's Best Developed Man)**

## Strength & Bulk Training
## for
## Weight Lifters & Body Builders

Any time the conversation turns to muscular bulk and power, the world famous name of Reg Park comes to mind. Reg brought physical development to a new high by winning the NABBA Mr. Universe three times and doing an impromptu bench press of over 500 lbs. at the 1957 Professional Mr. USA contest! He helped Bruce Randall prepare for and win the 1959 NABBA Mr. Universe. Park was the idol and mentor of the great Arnold Schwarzenegger! This is a modern reprint of Park's classic course detailing the *original* 5x5 training system, weight progression, diet, rest, record keeping, sticking points, limit poundages, single attempts, boredom, injuries and stress, attitude and exercises that Reg used to build his awesome size & strength. The course includes three different training routines for weight lifters and three for body builders. It demystifies how to make steady continual progress. An absolute must if you want huge gains in muscular bulk and power now! A classic course, fully illustrated.

This is the classic course from the golden era of weight training that established the connection between bodybuilding for aesthetic appeal and brute strength for functional purpose.

An absolute must if you want huge gains in muscular bulk and power now!

## Contents:

**Order today from:**

**Bill Hinbern**
**32430-K Cloverdale St.**
**Farmington, Michigan**
**48336-4008**
**USA**
**www.superstrengthtraining.com**
**info@superstrengthtraining.com**